THE
GOLDEN
KEY

A Story Biography of Nicolo Paganini

BY ELEANOR MAYNOR

Illustrated by Jack Gaughan

This is a vivid, convincing picture of a young musical genius — Nicolo Paganini at age fifteen — evoking his dreams, ambitions, and difficulties against the glowing background of Genoa in the late eighteenth century when Napoleon was emerging as a powerful figure.

The violin virtuoso is shown as he struggled to develop the new techniques and compositions with which he startled the musical world.

His friendships and response to the life around him convey all the despair and ecstasy of a great artist, while the homes of his benefactors, with their elaborate furnishings and lavish parties, offer a startling contrast to Paganini's own barefoot poverty.

This is a book that readers of all ages will not relinquish until they have read the last word on the last page.

A CRITERION BOOK
FOR YOUNG PEOPLE

THE GOLDEN KEY
A Story Biography
of
Nicolò Paganini

THE
GOLDEN
KEY

A Story Biography of Nicolò Paganini

BY ELEANOR MAYNOR

ILLUSTRATED BY JACK GAUGHAN

Criterion Books, Inc.
NEW YORK

To Asa, Marcia, Lee
and the memory of my Mother

1

At his accustomed spot in a section of the tarry wharf above the Bay of Genoa, in June, 1795, young Nicolò Paganini played the final number of his violin concert. With a bold brush stroke of the bow, he ended the composition to boisterous applause. Nicolò thrust a bare foot forward and bent low, his arm sweeping across his chest so that the bow stood high in the air above his left shoulder.

"Encore!" His listeners cheered. "Another, Nicolò! Just one more!" Urchins like himself, they lounged on the crumbling steps that ran down the middle of the street, or sat on the paving stones, their grimy feet thumping time to the music.

Nicolò stood erect, laughing. "*Grazie*," he said. "Thanks, *grazie*." He heard, more than felt, the soft breeze that slapped water against the pilings below. "Shh." He motioned with the bow to his lips. "Listen. . . ." Someday he'd write a concerto translating all these exciting sounds of Genoa to his own language! Music was as much a part of him as breathing!

"Shh." Someone heckled, good-naturedly. There were a few titters as the applause started again.

"Be quiet!" A boy urged from the steps. "Let him listen, if you want a surprise. At home, Nicolò will pull all sorts of sounds out of his fiddle, set down notes on every piece of paper he can find."

The speaker's voice was pushed out of his mind by the marvelous music in his head. Seagoing sounds from ships in the harbor mingled with the bustle of the nearby market square. Farther down the wharf, hearty shouts rang out as the *legabelle* corded up bales of cargo intended for ports in the East and America. From the tower of the black and white Duomo, Cathedral of San Lorenzo, rolled the resonant *bong* of the great bell. Overhead, washings from open windows of tall houses with peeling plaster flapped a lively *pizzicato*. Nicolò smiled. These sounds which he made into tunes and rhythms were as real as the smell of oranges, sea spray, and the pungent odor of the vats when young sheep's guts were boiled for the manufacture of violin strings.

". . . and then, tomorrow, we'll hear the cry of that gull out there." The boy on the steps pointed to a bird circling above the Mediterranean. "Or, maybe, the laughter of the *legabelle* down at the port!" Nicolò glanced uneasily toward the dock where his father, Antonio Paganini, worked as a *legabelle*, packer of olives and pickles.

"I've no more time," he said. "I should be practicing at home when my father arrives." Imagining he heard the familiar voice rising above the others', he wished that, sometimes, his father would bring his booming laughter to their cramped four-room house instead of leaving it at the wharf. At home, he was nearly always angry.

"Your imitations, Nicolò! Play your imitations!" This last from Germi, his friend and confidant who lived not far from him in the old quarter of the city known as the Passo.

Nicolò took a deep breath. It was barely possible that he could play a little longer and still get home ahead of his father. Rebellion stirring in him, he rosined up his bow, placed the violin under his chin, and began in rapid tempo. He imitated noises of the barnyard — grunting pigs, cackling hens, the braying of an ass, ending with the falsetto crowing of a cock at dawn. It wasn't music but it set his audience giggling and rolling over the steps.

As he replaced the little Amati in the cloth bag which his mother had made to hold the violin, he said happily: "Tomorrow, I'll play my own variations on *La Carmagnole*." More cheers went up, for the revolutionary song was still popular in sympathetic Genoa even though the end of the French Revolution and its terrors was now three years past.

A gay voice asked, "Do you know Mozart?" An instant hush spread warningly. Somebody snickered. Nicolò's mouth went dry.

"Of course, I know Mozart!" he said. "But I do not play Mozart!" A hot flush crept from his neck, bringing tears of fury to Nicolò's black eyes. He churned at the clumsy question. It was unnecessary! They all knew how he felt!

13

Suddenly, he realized that the speaker who sat apart was a stranger — a small, fair-haired girl with the face of one of Michelangelo's children in the Sistine Chapel. She wore shoes. She was clean. Nicolò wanted to touch her fine clothes. He disliked her at once.

"And you might as well understand something else!" he blurted. "Someday my name will be greater than Mozart's! I know of the fine little silk coats he wore when, at five, he entertained royalty! I know everything about him and I hate him!"

"Hate a dead man?" she asked, aghast. "What did he ever do to you?"

"— and I'll write music more beautiful than his! Besides, I'd rather not talk about it."

"More beautiful?" She added simply, "Beauty can't grow in a garden of hate."

"I said I'd rather not talk about it!"

Her eyes, dark as rosary beads, studied him without rancor, but she made no reply.

Crossing quickly to her side, he scowled. "What's your name?" His abrupt question sounded rude.

"Lisa," she told him gently. "Lisa Livron. From Leghorn." Her voice made him think of a silver bell. "I'm in Genoa with my father, who is here on a matter of business." The group around them began to dissolve.

"Nicolò!" Germi called. "Hurry, Nicolò! It's late."

Germi went up the steps and the girl arose. She was slight and not tall. The top of her shining head brushed Nicolò's chin.

"How old are you?" he asked.

14

"Sixteen."

"Why are you here? In this place — uh — on the wharf?"

"Because of you."

"You are joking!"

"You are modest!" she assured him. "Surely you know that news of the young Genoese virtuoso has spread to Leghorn?" As she spoke he noticed a dimple in her cheek. "I persuaded Father to bring me along because I've wanted to hear you play ever since you gave your first concert several years ago."

"Were you there?"

"No, unfortunately."

Nicolò decided that Lisa wasn't as bad as he had first thought. He would forgive her the Mozart question.

"When I was eight," he said, "I played a Pleyel concerto at the Duomo and another sacred concert last year. Oh, you should have been there! My name was on leaflets — this high!" He measured with thumb and finger.

A tall, well-built man hurried down the steps. "Ah, Lisa!" he called. "Is the concert over?" His eyes were kind. He would never take a strap to anyone, Nicolò thought ruefully.

"Father!" Lisa answered, lowering her voice when she spoke to Nicolò. "He's always wanted, so badly, to be a musician! Father, this is Paganini!" The big man's smile was good to see.

"The brilliant young genius whom all Genoa is raving about?" His handclasp was vigorous.

"My name is Nicolò, sir."

"Please —" Lisa touched her father's arm. "Tomorrow

15

Nicolò is playing his own variations. May we remain over-
night?" Livron turned to the boy before him for understanding.

"She knows I can't refuse her! So, we'll stay!"

In a flash Nicolò thought of his own father. And Germi,
already at the top of the steps, was glowering.

"Excuse me, sir." Nicolò picked up the bag. "I should be
at home. Good day to you both."

"Tomorrow, Nicolò," Lisa called after him.

Running up the steps, which his long legs took two at a
time, he informed Germi, "Her name is Lisa Livron. She
came just to listen to my music."

Germi's mouth flew open. "Livron, did you say? The
merchant of Leghorn?"

"And she's coming back tomorrow."

"He's rich! I've heard my family speak of him. He can
buy anything he wants!"

Nicolò looked down at his bare feet. "I wonder how
many pairs of shoes he owns."

"As many as he wants! He has a carriage, too — and
horses," Germi said with envy.

They hurried past the historic Casa di Colombo, house of
Christopher Columbus, passed under the twin-castellated
Porto Soprano, embattled entrance to the Old City, and
crossed the street. Ahead, over to the right, near the
Cathedral, was the ancient Palace of the Doges.

The skin crawled on the back of his neck as Nicolò
thought of his plans. Identifying himself with the romance
of Italy, its nobility, its villas, its music, he lived in his

private world even while Europe was overrun by war and plunder. And he firmly believed in the legend of his birth that his mother kept alive—the angel's promise that her son would become the greatest violinist in the world!

Nicolò spoke aloud. "One day I will listen to applause from kings and queens! I will receive many presents. Gloves of softest silk embroidered with gold threads."

They skirted a pile of refuse blocking the street, hastened across a corner of the Old Market where a fresh beef carcass, slit down the backbone, its ribs stretched out on either side, dangled from a pulley at the butcher's stall.

Thinking of the pasta at home, Nicolò continued: "And I will dine with important princes, ride in carriages with plum-red wheels and velvet insides and silver door handles. I'll be rich, very rich. I'll rule the earth!" To himself he said: "Most of all, most important of all, I will be loved!"

"*Amico mio!*" Germi brought him back sharply. "So what's strange about that? Everybody's got ruling on the brain. The revolutionists in Paris are ruling — finally!" He chopped the air with an open palm, rolling his eyeballs backward until only the whites showed. "But not before heads bounced red down the gutters while others stacked up in baskets at the foot of a bloody gibbet!" He laughed. "I like my head where it is!"

"War has always been around us," Nicolò answered. "There's been fighting of one kind or another always, in Italy. Italians fight each other, they fight at home, in the streets, at sea, in the hills —"

Germi interrupted. "My father says there will probably be more fighting. The new French republic in Paris will have to protect its frontiers. Besides, it's time somebody got rid of those Austrians in the north for us. My father also says that we haven't heard the last of that astounding young General Buonaparte."

"I've heard of him. They call him — Napoleon? What's so astounding about him?" Nicolò wanted to know.

"He's young. And he's just made monkeys out of the British at Toulon, that's all! Now he's bent on command of the Italian frontier if he can gain the favor of Carnot, the French War Minister."

"I hope he gets it!" Nicolò exclaimed. "Now, why waste our breath on war and politics? Let's talk about something important — like music." And he waited for Germi to smile so that he could see his friend's eyes crinkle at the corners. As usual, this gave Germi a ridiculous expression. Nicolò giggled and said he wouldn't trade places with Napoleon, or with anybody, for that matter. "Thank goodness, I don't have to depend on artillery or armies or war ministers! I can take over the world with disguised weapons."

"What are you babbling about, Nicolò? What weapons?"

For someone who could read and write, Germi was certainly stupid about some things. Nicolò explained, patiently, *"Legato, staccato, spiccato.* Music, silly! My territories will be captured with a fiddle. There won't be a soul who hasn't heard of Paganini."

"Since the smashing victory at Toulon, there are few who haven't heard of Napoleon. They speak of him with fear and with hope," Germi said.

"They'll speak of me with amazement and praise. Anyhow, Napoleon's French."

"He's not! He's the same as you — Italian — from Corsica."

19

"But he's a French general. And you prattle about him freeing Italy from Austria?" Nicolò threw up his free hand. "Who can understand that?" He added, as an afterthought, "Somebody does, I guess. . . . They're saying around the state buildings that he's power-hungry."

"Ha! Well, so are you!" Germi stuck his hands in his pockets. Facing Nicolò, he walked backward.

"Depends on the kind of power. My smashing victories won't include treaties, boundaries, flags, or terror. Not a shot will be fired. Just sounds . . . glorious sounds that will melt people and leave them powerless to move."

"You really mean it, don't you?" Germi's voice had wonder in it. He stopped suddenly so that Nicolò ran right into him.

"Ugg — umprff! Of course I mean it," Nicolò assured him as, heads only inches apart, they snickered at each other cross-eyed.

"I hope I'm here to see all of this take place! You have lots of notes up there in your head, but you don't make any other kind of sense!"

"Turn around so you can see where you're going."

"I know where I'm going!" Germi darted off.

"Where?"

"Home. To supper. Later on to Parliament, as an advocate!"

And that gave Nicolò the idea. He caught up with Germi. "*Amico caro*," he said. "We are friends?"

"What's that got to do with anything?" Germi asked.

"You know I can't read or write very well. My father is anxious for me to study music, nothing else."

"You can sign your name at least!" Germi muttered, as they turned left under an arch of blushing oleander.

"That's not enough." Nicolò shifted the violin bag from one hand to the other. "When I am the world's greatest violinist, I'll need someone to take care of important things. A business manager to handle my affairs." He didn't quite know what he meant by it all, but it sounded intriguing, mysterious. "Because you are my friend and you are reading law and you know *everything* —" His eyes were glistening. "I offer you the job — now. Do you accept?" Nicolò took a small knife from his pocket.

"Why the knife?" Germi scratched his head.

"We draw each other's blood. We make a pact. And then we're bound together!"

Germi leaned against the side of a dilapidated building whose walls, the color of faded violets, were traced by clinging ivy. He pursed his lips. "I haven't accepted—yet!"

"Well, I can't wait all day!" Nicolò closed the knife. "The offer is withdrawn."

"*Un momento, un momento!*" Germi grinned. "I accept." He extended his arm. Nicolo slashed quickly with a light, sure stroke. A bright red trickle stained the blade. He handed the knife to Germi who said:

"Look the other way. You're only fifteen!"

"Sixteen in October!" Nicolò's eyes flashed. "I guess eighteen is ancient." He cleared his throat. "Since we are going to be partners for life, please don't start out by referring to my age." He watched without flinching as Germi executed his part of the bargain. They touched forearms, smearing blood. Nicolò wiped the blade on his trousers, returning the knife to his pocket. "We will tour to distant places—as far as England. We will meet people who don't even know who Mozart is!"

"*Bene*—good." The practical Germi was content to leave it at that. "But—now—tonight?" He ran off down an alleyway that led to his house.

"And I'll wear Moroccan slippers, a fine cloak!" Nicolò was jerked out of his dream by the gurgling obligato of a drainpipe ejecting its muck.

2

He bolted. It was only a short distance through the steep quarter of narrow alleys to his home. He knew by the slight chill of early evening that he was later than usual, and he determined to invoke the prayers of the Madonna to allay his father's anger.

Breathing hard, he skidded to a stop before the building where he lived. It was similar to the others around it—tall and slim, its façade weathered to a light rose. A tiny niche imbedding the house front held a little Madonna in a setting of plaster flowers and fruit. Nicolò crossed himself, recited a hasty litany. He finished, "Oh, blessed Mother, *perdone,* I'm in a hurry."

Without stopping for breath, he went quickly up the three flights of stone steps worn hollow in the center. Upon opening the door, he was assailed by kitchen odors, blended with the smell of the wharfs. Cat bounded forward on cushioned feet and rubbed his legs. When she had followed him home, not long ago, his father had growled, "Another mouth to feed?" At his plea, "She won't eat much," surprisingly, his father replied nothing more than, "I don't like them — cats! Keep this one out of my way." This wasn't hard to do, for the animal adopted Nicolò immediately, remained indifferent to the others.

His sisters, Domenicia and Nicoletta, along with Carlo, his elder brother, were already at the table, stuffing them-selves. They kept right on eating but their sidelong glances said, You're in trouble, Nicolò!

Antonio Paganini, a mountain of flesh, whirled from the pump. "You're late again!" he said. "Where've you been?" Stripped to the waist, he was soaping his hairy chest.

"Giving a concert, sir." Nicolò laid aside the violin and waited. However, the leather strap remained untouched. His father must have won in the lottery today, or else the little Madonna had managed a quick prayer to heaven. After all, he had said he was in a hurry! Nicolò thanked her silently, just in case, and eased into his chair as his mother turned from the stove.

"Ah, my baby! Ah, Nicolò!" She kissed him with her glance and pushed the steaming pasta across the table. "So pale! So thin!" She looked at his father, who was splash-ing water over his head and shoulders. Rubbing himself dry with an old towel, Antonio threw it in a corner and sat down, attacking his food.

"Harbor concerts!" he sneered. "And not a lira to show

24

for it!" Nicolò dug his nails into his palm. He knew the next by heart.

"Mozart —" his father spoke as if he were saying it for the first time — "Mozart composed a minuet and a trio when he was five!" Antonio brought his fist down with a bang. The oil lamp sputtered and belched smoke at the ceiling. "And a concerto at eight."

Nicolò ground his teeth. He cried, inside: I played a concert at eight. Can't you say anything about that? Isn't that worth mentioning? All of a sudden, he wasn't hungry. He pushed back his plate.

"Why aren't you eating? Food not good enough?" His father wasn't going to let up. "Well, now, if you were more like Mozart there could be fried octopus, red chianti—food and drink worthy of the house of Paganini!" He broke off a chunk of hard-crusted bread.

Not daring to reply, Nicolò tried to look respectful. Carlo's gaze sought his face, but his brother said nothing. The girls bent their heads over their plates. Cat purred against his foot under the table.

"Please — leave him alone!" His mother was brave when you least expected it. "Give the boy time!"

"Time? How much does he need?" Antonio took big mouthfuls, chewed with his mouth open. "Mozart's sheet music brought in revenue when he was only twelve. His family took scented baths — and I wash at the pump!" Wiping his chin with his thumb, he licked it clean.

Nicolò played with his food. It gave him something to do as he phrased his defense. "Around the docks," he said, "I've heard that Mozart died so poor he had to be buried in a pauper's cemetery . . . somewhere near Vienna, in an unmarked grave."

"Don't argue with me!" his father shouted.

Nicolò clamped his lips together. Why had he bothered? His father emphasized only the few years of Mozart's life that were luxurious. To admit to anything else wouldn't serve his purpose.

"And the vision promised —" His mother's sentence was cut short.

"The vision? Of course, the vision!" Antonio waved his fork. "Nevertheless, I will see to it that my son is the greatest violinist in the world!" He spoke of Nicolò as though he weren't in the room. "The boy is lucky to have me for a father. If things had been different with me. . . ." His voice descended to a whisper. "It's possible I might be playing tonight in the great red and gold Scala in Milan." Nicolò met his eyes and glanced quickly away. He had witnessed something it was unfair to see. At that moment color flamed Antonio's face. Recovering, he finished loudly, "Instead of being listed in the town register as a mandolin player! With a tavern floor for a stage—where playing is for fun—and my audience a bunch of loudmouths who can't even carry a tune!"

Nicolò watched his mother. Her eyes were too bright. In a moment she would sob. The routine was always the same: his father's ravings, his own angry silences, his mother's tears. And his father didn't really feel that way about the taverns. He met his friends, often, in one of the old Saracen hideouts to accompany their merry songs. At the same time, he picked up tips on coming lotteries. No, it wasn't the taverns. It was he, Nicolò, and Mozart, and too little laughter, and the pump, and not enough food. Antonio was speaking again.

"Ever thought of yourself with a Stradivari? I hope to live to see one in your hands, Nicolò!" It was a burst of confidence. It was salve on a wound.

"You will, someday, Father. I promise you. You will!"

"It's the only instrument a virtuoso should play! Do you think you'll ever be able to buy such a fine violin?"

"Certainly!" That was an absurd question. "I'll be rich enough to buy anything, presents for everybody!" Too late, he realized he'd fallen neatly into the trap.

"Not by playing harbor concerts, or solos in San Lorenzo on Sundays, you won't!" Antonio was glowering again.

His mother gave way, putting her hands to her face. She spoke through her fingers. "But that's how he pays for his lessons — by playing in the Cathedral on Sundays!"

"Don't tell me something I already know!" Antonio sopped bread in his plate. "I arranged all of that with Signor Costa."

"Besides," she sobbed, "he is still such a baby." The girls slipped away from the table as Carlo let himself out of the door. Nicolò didn't blame them. If he could, he'd get away, too.

"He isn't a baby. When Mozart was —"

"Mozart! Mozart! Can't you ever stop talking about Mozart?" Nicolò jumped up, overturning his chair. Antonio's face was black. He reached for the strap, twirling it around his hand.

"Come here, Nicolò!" he said.

"No — no!" His mother flew around the table, pushing Nicolò behind her, motioning to his plate. "You see — he hasn't eaten tonight!" She hesitated. "He must be — sick."

"I'm not sick." Nicolò stepped aside. "I just don't want to hear another word about Mozart."

Antonio let the strap swing free. Apparently, the moment had passed. "Get!" he ordered, frowning. "To your practicing!" Nicolò scooped up Cat, took his violin, and went obediently from the table.

Once he shut himself inside his closet-sized bedroom, his spirits soared, the scene with his father was forgotten. Lighting the lamp, he lifted the violin from its case and plucked the strings, creating chords as a new score began to form around the sound of Lisa's silver-bell laughter. Knowing that the composition would perfect itself in his brain if he allowed it to simmer, he put it out of his mind for the time being, and began practicing. An étude, special effects; harmonics in doubles, and stopping the *staccati* short by cutting off the vibration, a gavotte with improvised variations. He played a passage over with every known fingering, then invented methods of his own. Recalling that his first teacher, Servetto, preferred exercises in which the fingers remained on the strings, Nicolò tried placing one finger on top of the other while sustaining the melody. Straining his joints, he made a note to perfect the method. His fingering would be unique, he resolved, as well as his music. An entirely new, unusual kind of music!

Exhausted and wringing wet, he bounced the bow against the strings in a final shower of staccato notes, then collapsed in a chair. After a moment, he rested his left elbow on the table to study his hand. In attempting to make the third finger reach below the cushioned, fatty part at the base of the thumb, he felt a distinct pull from the wrist. He spoke aloud to his fingers.

"You'll soon be flexible enough," he said, "to perform exercises on the strings that no one believes possible! And people from all over will clamor for the most extraordinary Paganini." Nicolò chuckled. So they hadn't heard the last of Napoleon? Ha! If they only knew it, they hadn't heard the last of one called Nicolò, either. . . . Napoleon? If all predictions concerning the General came true, they would rise to fame together. Two astounding men, Paganini and Napoleon, each a conqueror in his chosen field. He stood up, stretched, walked around the table to lean on the sill of the open window. The sea basked in moonlight. And now that there was no one to interrupt, he thought about his other friend. . . .

He had never told a soul, not even Germi, about his adventure, three years ago, when he took a trip with his grandfather to Vienna, shortly before the old man's death. It was the only time he'd been away from home, and he found the elegant city dazzling. University buildings glittered white and the Duomo of St. Stephen's, raising its tower above venerable trees, looked almost as close to heaven as the Cathedral of San Lorenzo, at home.

To use up time while waiting for his grandfather, Nicolò had taken his violin to the park across the street from the Imperial Theater to practice his scales. Trees wore the fresh green of early spring, and in the branches above him

a family of birds twittered and scolded, occasionally burst into notes, threatening to outdo him. Nicolò paused, enjoying the sounds, when, not far off, he saw a young man studying him intently. The stranger was short, with a large head of black hair, shaggy and unconfined. Nicolò laughed. Indicating the birds, he said:

"One day I'll put those trills into my own composition."

Without waiting for a reply, he began a simple aria, playing with warmth and feeling, keeping the melody in birdlike harmonics. Just before he reached the end, he lowered the bow to listen again to the pure-throated song above him. The young man strode angrily across the grass.

"Finish the melody, please!" He spoke very bad Italian with a thick Rhenish accent, but at least he was trying to make himself understood in Italian. His face was ruddy and pockmarked. The high neckcloth he wore gave him a stiff, defiant air. "Finish it, do you hear? You must!" It sounded like a plea, nonetheless it was almost violent.

Nicolò stiffened. He asked, flatly, "Why?"

"Why?" The stranger's eyebrows drew together in a scowl. "Because cutting off the end like that is as painful to me as cutting off the end of my finger. Please — finish it!" Now it was a plea and Nicolò obliged, even adding a few variations.

The stranger smiled. His teeth were large, evenly spaced. "Ah!" he murmured.

Nicolò exclaimed, "You're a musician, too?"

The stranger's eyes danced. "In a way," he agreed.

"Do you live here?" Nicolò waved the bow. "In Vienna?"

31

"This is my home, now. I was born in Bonn, on the Rhine."

That would account for his peculiar accent, Nicolò thought, as he asked: "Have you lived here long?"

"Only a few months, this time. Five years ago, I was here for a short time to receive lessons in composition from Mozart."

"Mozart!" A muscle twitched in Nicolò's cheek. "My father beats me because I am not like Mozart!"

The young man shrugged. "I used to think I was the only one."

"Only one what?" Nicolò restored violin and bow to the bag.

The stranger changed the subject. "How old are you?"

Nicolò stood tall. "Twelve," he said.

"You're quite accomplished. You must have been playing since you were a baby."

"I have never been a baby. I cut my first tooth on salami." More soberly, "I'll be great whether he beats me or not. And my fame will spread farther than Mozart's."

There was no reproach in the other's face. No surprise, either. He said, "I know —"

"You do?" Nicolò's face showed his surprise. They sat on the ground, backs against the bole of a tree. Nicolò prodded, "Go on."

"At times, I think I must have hated my father," the stranger said.

"I don't hate my father. I just hate Mozart."

"You'll change your mind one day, as I did. When you've thought it out."

Nicolò knew he would never change his mind and said so, adding quickly, "I won't interrupt again. I'm sorry."

His new friend chewed a blade of grass as he continued: "My father forced me to practice for hours at a time when I was so small I had to stand on a footstool to reach the clavier. If I cried because my legs ached, he related tales of Empress Marie-Theresa, how she rocked the infant Mozart on her knee along with her own baby daughter, the unfortunate Marie Antoinette, how she showered the boy genius with kisses and gold." He spat out the grass. "My father used to say to me, 'If Mozart can do it, you can do it,' determined to make me the solution to his money problems."

Nicolò crossed his legs. "Did he beat you, too?"

"Sometimes. Also, he brought his friends home late from the wine houses and pulled me out of bed to perform until sunrise. I was so sleepy I couldn't see the keys!"

This man understood his own kind of misery! Nicolò's heart quickened. He'd found a friend! Someone older who treated him as if they were the same age. Now he wasn't ashamed to ask the question!

"Why," he said, "did you study composition under him — under Mozart? Couldn't you find another teacher?"

"Oh, yes!" His friend laughed. "But you see, I preferred to study with — *him!*"

"Why?"

"For many reasons. Not the least because his form was perfect." Shifting his position, he supported himself on his arm. "I left Vienna because my mother was ill, and I have just returned. Alas, Mozart is gone!"

Nicolò was tired of the subject. It seemed the name of Mozart plagued him everywhere. He asked, "Are you studying now?"

"Yes. With a master — Haydn."

"He's been abroad! To London!" Nicolò narrowed his eyes. "Are you learning anything?"

"Well — yes and no. His genius isn't communicable. But I've learned enough to know that I want to write a new kind of composition. I want my work to be thunder and lightning as well as sunshine. Do you know what I'm talking about?"

"Of course! It's simple. I too intend to make up music never heard before. But you don't need lessons for that! Lessons are rules. I don't like rules."

"Who does?" The man lowered his voice. "I've never wanted to pay attention to rules, either. But I think I must learn my craft before I explore new techniques. Does that make sense?"

"That part of it does. What about the thunder and lightning?"

"Ah! That's something else again. That comes from here —" He touched his chest. "One has to feel before he can make others feel. Music must tell of both the joy and the sadness that live in the heart."

A carriage rolled to a stop at the end of the street. The driver jumped down from the box. He motioned to Nicolò as the spirited horses stamped impatiently. The boy took his violin and scrambled to his feet.

"Good-bye!" he exclaimed. "That's my grandfather. Good-bye!" He was halfway across the grass when he

34

turned and ran back. "Sir," he cried, "I forgot to ask your name! My new friend — and I don't even know your name!"

The man smiled. "I am Ludwig Beethoven."

3

Nicolò was in the carriage beside his grandfather before he shrieked, "*Beethoven!* Grandfather! In the park—that man—"

"Beethoven? Well, now!" The old man chuckled as he made room on the seat. "Sit back. Tell me—" The carriage bounced and jolted over the stones as Nicolò related the events of the morning. While he talked he was excitingly aware of the crunching noise of the wheels turning in response to the horses' flying feet. Now — if he could bounce the bow away from the strings in *staccati* and at the same time keep a deeper overtone — then he would have this same moving-forward sound in his music. The only trouble was. . . .

After he had told his grandfather all about his encounter,

he said, almost to himself, "There must be one, somewhere, with a sterner voice."

"Eh?" his grandfather questioned. "I don't follow you, lad."

"I was just saying that I wish I could find a violin with a strong-willed voice. Firm — deep." Touching the case between them, he announced, "This little Amati's too light-toned, too soft and sweet."

"Nicolò! What goes on in your head! Too soft and sweet for what?"

Nicolò laughed, "For some of the music that goes on in my head!"

His grandfather's eyes widened. He said, "Sometimes I have to stop and remember that you're still a boy! No matter," he went on, "I think the time has come to give —" he explored his pockets, first one and the other — "I have it here, somewhere. . . ."

"A present — for me?" Nicolò leaned over. "Is it? Tell me!" Then he settled back in his corner. "No — don't! Not yet!" His grandfather would take his time anyway, and that made the surprise last longer.

"You reminded me, with your talk of a violin with a deep voice. There are a few of them, you know. Very fine. Made by Guarneri."

"Guarneri?" Nicolò tingled. "I thought nothing was finer than Stradivari! My father says it's the only instrument a virtuoso should play!"

"And so do I! Just the same —" his grandfather was dead serious —"for some of the strange Paganini music you manage to extract from a fiddle you do need an instrument

37

with a coarser tone." They entered a glade, green and fragrant with spring.

"What's happened to them — the Guarneris?" Nicolò questioned. "Where are they? How can I find one?"

"Consider yourself lucky if you do! There weren't many. Most were sold elsewhere. The few, in Italy, are in the possession of millionaires."

"And Grandfather," Nicolò persisted, "how will I know it's a Guarneri if I see one?"

"Nicolò! If you'll stop talking long enough, I'll tell you." He licked his lips. "But not till we've eaten!" He brought out salami, a couple of *panini* (bread rolls), and dark red grapes.

They were in the hill country now. The carriage careened down a slope, then proceeded slowly, picking its ruts on the bad roads. The day was warm, yellow with sunshine. Nicolò opened his jacket. He ate heartily.

His grandfather handed him a jug of light wine. "Wash it down, boy."

Nicolò waited until the remnants of food were put away before he spoke. "Did Guarneri live in Cremona, too — the home of the other craftsmen?"

"Yes." His grandfather wiped his lips. "In Cremona, where the first violins were constructed, as you know, by the Amati family. But the most remarkable Amati of them all devised a secret varnish formula."

"Secret formula? How do you know?"

"From an old, old story. And from what I remember."

"Remember!" Nicolò waited an eternity for the next sentence."

"Amati's dearest friend was your ancestor, whom he called 'Oldpag', running it all together in one word."

"Oldpag!" Nicolò breathed out the word. His very own ancestor, the famous Amati, and a secret varnish formula!

"Now —" His grandfather held up two fingers. "Among the pupil apprentices were a couple of youths, Antonio Stradivari and Andrea Guarneri, who worked very hard. Their chores were many, for after the sheep's guts were boiled, peeled, and pickled, they hung on wooden frames to bleach in sulphur fumes. Finally, they were polished in almond oil before being cut into proper lengths. This was a long and messy process."

"And does it smell!" Nicolò held his nose. "Phewww!" He laughed. "Go on — about Oldpag."

"He and Amati, these two old friends, gambled at cards almost every day in a room of Amati's basement shop. And sometimes the curious apprentices would step inside to watch. Naturally, this wasn't permitted by Amati. One day he scolded Guarneri, 'Back to your chores!' but allowed Stradivari to remain beside the table. Oldpag was especially fond of Guarneri and thought this partiality was cruel and unfair. As soon as they were alone again, he said so.

"Amati replied, 'Stradivari's violins will be praised throughout Italy and the world! Mark my words! He is my favorite pupil, and when I die, I intend to leave him all my belongings — models, tools, choice wood, formula.'

"That's when Oldpag had an idea."

"What, Grandfather? What happened next? Please go on."

"Nicolò! I must catch my breath!"

The old man studied the passing landscape before he went on. "Oldpag dealt the cards and dared Amati to wager his varnish formula against a certain sum of money which he named. Amati was furious. He sputtered, 'Why should I wager my precious formula? What would you do with it if you won?' He waved his hand. 'The idea is ridiculous!'

"Oldpag leaned back in his chair. He answered, 'I'd give it to Guarneri.'

"Amati considered this. 'You are willing to chance the loss of all that money for the sake of the lad?'

" 'Yes. Because I believe in him.' Oldpag rubbed his hands together. 'Besides, I expect to win.'

"Amati found a spot on the ceiling. 'Ha!' he said. 'I do, too! So I must decide if I really want your money. I already have everything I need. I'll probably never live to spend it, anyway!'

"Oldpag shrugged his shoulders. 'Then the formula will go to Stradivari, along with everything else.' Indicating the cards on the table, he added, 'Of course, if you're afraid, if you've lost your nerve —'

"Amati was not one to deny himself the pleasure of a bet. 'You speak like a fool!' he said and picked up the cards. 'What are we waiting for?' "

Nicolò sucked in his breath. "What happened, Grandfather? Who won?"

"Oldpag, of course!" His grandfather slapped his knee. "And Amati took it like a man. He shouted for Guarneri to come at once.

41

" 'Before you tell him,' Oldpag whispered hurriedly, 'before he gets here, promise not to divulge my part in this. That is my secret.' "

Nicolò sighed happily. "He did that, Grandfather? A Paganini did that — many years ago?" His heart swelled with pride for this magnificent ancestor of his, who had left him a magnificent heritage. Nicolò's head throbbed with mysterious music, and he saw himself grown straight and tall, before the footlights, drawing the bow across the strings of a deep-throated Guarneri, full toned and mellow as a beautiful speaking voice. Little shivers of delight ran through him.

His grandfather was saying, "Amati took Guarneri to a far side of the room, extracting a vow that he would reveal the formula to no one except his own heirs, and made him memorize the ingredients so they would never have to be written down. And that is probably why the proportions are lost today. Even the identity of the fifth ingredient is still a mystery. Amati said, 'Put it in your head, where you know it's safe.' "

Nicolò asked, "Did Oldpag hear any of this?"

"Actually, Oldpag had no intention of eavesdropping, but snatches of the conversation reached him. Amati wasn't whispering — right then, that is — and Oldpag heard him say, 'Thick turpentine, transparent amber, linseed oil, and above all — tender gum. It isn't one varnish, but *two* varnishes.' Then he whispered something in the boy's ear."

"What?" Nicolò could hardly breathe.

"Ah! That's something no one will ever know! The formula died many years later with his grandson, the most famous

Joseph Del Gesu Guarneri, who signed the initials I.H.S. on all his labels."

"Why did he do that?" This was the most exciting conversation in the world!

"The sacred monogram was often attached to works of art. Joseph used it to distinguish himself from other members of his family who also made violins."

"Because he thought his violins were the best?"

"Not necessarily. However, he was proud and grateful that only he possessed the formula. Because of it, perhaps, his violins are considered by some to be the finest ever made."

"Better than the Stradivari?"

"Some people think so."

"Why?" Nicolò was drinking in every word.

"The tone of his violin is more vigorous, penetrating. Tone was the main quality sought by Joseph. You see, perfection of form and style had already been attained by Stradivari—his instruments are accurate and scientific, with true geometrical curves in the slanting *f*'s and graceful side *c*'s. Sponsored by influential men, Stradivari worked hard, made many violins, and was executing some of his best work when Joseph del Gesu was still a young man." His grandfather continued after a pause. "Ah!" he said. "This craftsman was quite another matter. His violins were made by ear!"

"Now you're teasing me!"

"No, I'm not! He'd go into the woods with a little hammer —"

"Hammer? What for?"

"Before any tree was felled, he'd tap against the trunk, make his selection by the sound." His grandfather promised, "If you ever see or touch a Del Gesu, God willing, you'll know it!"

"How?" Nicolo asked eagerly. He could listen to this kind of talk all day.

"Guarneri never took accurate measurements, or worked with regard to uniformity of appearance, size, or design. He was led by his own genius and theories which he proved by experiment. A careless master! His f holes are slashed almost at random! And, of course, in addition to the rugged build, he captured the tone you spoke of — powerful, robust."

Nicolò vowed to himself that someday, somehow, he would find a precious, deep-throated Guarneri. Wrinkling his forehead, he said, "Did you ever know him, Grandfather?"

"No — not really. But I saw him once when I was a lad . . . in prison."

"*Prison?*" Nicolò almost leaped from his seat. "Guarneri in prison? Why?"

The old man sighed. "A technicality of law of which he was unaware — an unfortunate circumstance from which he was unable to extricate himself."

Nicolò swallowed. "Was he put to torture?"

"No. At least he was spared that. When the powerful Duke of Parma learned his identity, he ordered the prisoner to make several violins, arranging for the necessary materials to be brought to his cell. There he worked, half-starved, confined in a space crawling with vermin."

"Poor man!"

"That's exactly how the jailer's daughter felt. She sat outside his cell, played the mandolin, sang funny songs to make him laugh. Guarneri looked forward to her visits; he depended on them. She was the only star in his black sky, and after he had finished the Duke's violins he made one for her with material he had saved and kept hidden. These violins, these 'prison Josephs' as they were referred to, were naturally crudely constructed; sort of off balance. The *f*'s appeared to be cut with a dull knife."

Nicolò was incredulous. "Did you see them?"

"Only the one he made for the jailer's daughter. When I went to the prison with my father to cheer his old friend, Del Gesu showed the instrument to us with great pride. I remember the broad scroll of the head, the magnificent thick tone. When he plucked the strings, it rolled out, filling the cell until the very stones seemed to vibrate. The label was roughly engraved on a wooden block."

"I wonder where her violin is today."

"Lost, I presume. Lost forever. Del Gesu died in 1744, shortly after our visit. He was penniless, of course, and the disconsolate girl sold the precious Guarneri to buy a headstone for his grave." The old man shifted his position before he went on. "You know, he must have known that day that he was going to die soon, for he said to me, 'I may never know another Paganini. I'd like you to have this —'"

Nicolò's glance darted to the old man's pocket. "He gave you a present?" His heart was beating fast. A present from the famous Joseph del Gesu — and a while ago, he himself had been promised a present.

His grandfather was aware of Nicolò's excitement.

"You're already ahead of me, aren't you, boy? Yes — this is the present. From Del Gesu to me, and now from me to you!"

Nicolò gasped at the sight of the little snuffbox that lay in his open palm. Tiny colored squares incrusted the surface — rose, pale blue, lilac — set between threadlike gold wire fillets. "See," his grandfather said, "it opens like this. You can carry your rosin in it." His face sobered. "Keep it with you, Nicolò. And remember, it will always bring you good luck!"

Nicolò wanted to laugh, he wanted to cry, he wanted to throw his arms around the old man's neck, but all he said was, "Oh, Grandfather!"

"Well, now." The old man yawned elaborately. "Put it away, boy, in your case. I've talked much too long. Nearly passed up my *riposo!*" He put his head back against the seat and was soon snoring loudly. . . .

The sudden shrill bark of a dog brought Nicolò back from his memories. He was cold. He didn't know how long he'd been standing at the window. The moon was a slice of lemon, and far out, over the water, the sky glowed pink. Quickly stripping off his clothes, he scrambled into bed and closed his eyes.

4

Nicolò awoke with a start and sprang from bed. Already there was a late feeling to the day. Wet clothes snapped in the wind on the lines outside his window, laughter floated up from the street, and Cat narrowed her eyes impatiently, as if to say, "Well, it's about time!" He grabbed his clothes from the floor where he'd left them the night before and dressed hurriedly. Lisa would be waiting! Tuning the violin, he placed it in the case, and made sure that the little snuffbox was inside.

When he turned the doorknob, alarm shot through him. The door held fast. Nicolò yanked and tugged but it was no use. He was locked in! Not today — no, not today! He kicked in despair. Another time it wouldn't have mattered so much. Believing that diligent practice was the natural result of confinement, his father frequently locked him in

47

his room. "I am building a musician," he would say over his wife's protests.

Nicolò crossed to the window, salt air strong in his nostrils. He glanced through the gaily colored wash flapping between the buildings, past tenement windows cluttered with hanging salami and red tomatoes, to the street below. Germi should be coming along any minute. Ah! There he was, rounding the corner, and in a few seconds would pass directly underneath. Nicolò called down:

"Germi! I'm locked in!"

"Again?" Germi swung around on one foot, reversing his steps. *"Arrivederci!"*

"Basta! Stop!" Nicolò had to shout for the wind pushed his voice back down his throat. "Come up, talk to Mamma, get me out of this place!"

"And account to your father later? You should have better sense!"

"Remember the pact, Germi!" Lisa was probably even now at the wharf. Lisa! This special, clean, pretty girl whose remark yesterday, concerning beauty, was gnawing at him in a manner which he couldn't define.

"Pact or no pact —" Germi shaded his eyes to look up — "there's still your father."

"Then get on!" Nicolò said. "I herewith dismiss you as my manager. I never want to see you again!"

Several persons gathered around Germi were enjoying the scene. Someone shouted, "Why don't you jump, Paganini? We'll catch you. You may break a leg, but all you need are your arms, anyhow!" Their humor escaped Nicolò. Hanging farther out the window, his long curls blowing straight out behind, his pale face showing his anger, he glowered at Germi but could not maintain a fierce dignity because of the clothes flapping across his line of vision.

"You can't dismiss me!" Squinting at the glare, Germi shook his fist. "We've smeared blood!"

"Then get up here and do as you're told!"

Germi kicked a stone. "As your advocate —" he called out.

"As my what?" A bright orange shirt flipped its tail across Nicolò's mouth.

"As your advocate —" Germi cupped his hands to his lips — "your manager, I must warn you that you'll get the devil!"

Nicolò peeled off the wet shirttail. "If you don't get me out of here, you'll think *I am* the devil!" This ultimatum restoring his self-respect, he left the window and pressed his ear to the door in time to hear his mother say:

"Germi, *mio caro,* come in! Nicolò, poor baby, is locked in his room." Her voice was fighting tears.

"That's why I came up. You're the only one who can help us." Germi spoke with a bravado Nicolò knew he did not feel.

"His father said he must stay in his room all day. I'm not even to take food to him." She sniffed. "Us?"

"Yes! Last evening we swore a partnership. Look."

"Germi!" she gasped. "You've cut your arm!" So like his mother — to make a fuss over a mere scratch!

"With a knife — both of us — and smeared blood. Now we're bound together, forever."

50

"You've always been good friends. Friendship doesn't need swearing to."

"Tell her, Germi!" Nicolò yelled through the door. "The rest of it. Your new job—" His voice rose an octave. "Mamma, unlock the door, please! I'm tired of screaming!"

Footsteps approached the door. "I suppose there's no harm. . . ." A key turned, his mother entered, arms went around his neck. He'd never realized how small she was. No taller than Lisa.

"My poor Nicolò!" Her voice caught in a sob. She held him close and he had the odd notion that he was the comforter.

Behind her, Germi moved his lips silently, *"Be quiet."* Nicolò's heart stopped hammering against his chest. Germi had thought of something! Germi was hatching a scheme to free him.

"La Bocciardi —" his friend used the impressive formality of his mother's name—"allow me to present myself as Nicolò's new business manager!" He couldn't have been more dignified if he'd worn a wig.

"Manager?" She turned. "Nicolò?" The sob was gone, replaced by a lively curiosity. "Whatever are you talking about?" She was especially pretty when she smiled.

They sat on the bed facing Germi as he announced seriously: "As the world's greatest violinist, Nicolò must think only of his music. In other matters, he desires that I speak for him." Germi acted as though he were already in Parliament. "And that is why I am courteously requesting his release."

51

"Germi, you have the gallantry of a Doge!" A fine line appeared between her eyebrows and she pressed little creases in her coarse black skirt. "But you ask the impossible. His father— Never in all my life have I disobeyed his father."

Germi shook his head slowly, from side to side. "It pains me for you to think that I ask you to belittle his father's authority!" I must remind him, Nicolò thought, to burn two candles to square that one. "But —" Germi gestured with both hands — "Nicolò is due at the wharf today for a concert."

"Isn't he due there every day for a concert?" A little smile hovered at her lips.

"This one is special."

"Special?"

"They're all special!" Germi's eyes crinkled at the corners. "Can you imagine a virtuoso not appearing for his concert?"

You had to admit one thing about Germi, he didn't fool around. But, Nicolò told himself, I'm no better off and it's later all the time!

Then Germi said, "Will you tell us again the story of the vision?"

Nicolò stared, open-mouthed. Germi had taken leave of his senses! There were appropriate occasions to speak of the dream, but now was hardly the time. When he started to protest, Germi silenced him with a look.

"The vision?" his mother said. "Germi! You know that story as well as I do. Everybody on the wharfs, the market, the Cathedral — they all know it!" She squeezed Nicolò's hand. "Do *you* want to hear it, my Nicolò?" There was a glow about her. She seemed lighted from within. Sudden warmth flooded him, blotting out the afternoon, the concert, Lisa, Germi. . . . There was only the promise of his new life — his future.

"Yes — yes," he whispered.

His mother began, a little breathlessly. "When Nicolò was nearly five years old, I was sitting alone one late afternoon, watching the orange-red sunset; it was the color of fire. I must have fallen asleep, for the next thing I knew I was in a large, gloomy theater — the upper boxes hung with rich tapestries of birds, foliage, the walls echoing with mysterious music. As my eyes grew accustomed to the half-darkness, I recognized Nicolò as the soloist. The maestro, conducting the orchestra, was surrounded by a shining halo."

Whatever had been Germi's purpose for this thrilling story was apparently forgotten. He sat on the floor, knees pulled up under his chin, eyes gleaming. Hardly seeming to breathe, he listened intently. Outside, the noises from the street were softened by the boisterous wind, inducing the gulls to cease their wrangling. The whole world waited — waited for Nicolò's mother to go on. When she spoke again, her voice was lower.

"There was a chorus — thousands of voices. And then an ugly, dark person slipped up behind Nicolò. He was dressed in red, with horns on his brow. I screamed as the stage burst into flames! Curling black smoke filled my mouth, my lungs—and just when I knew I would suffocate, the ceiling split to expose a line of bright blue sky." She clasped her

53

hands in her lap as she continued. "I began to run, stumbling about in the reddish haze of charred wood flakes that floated everywhere. Then I saw the angel. It lifted me to the blackened roof where a seraph sounded a golden trumpet. And this time, the choir sang a hymn. At its close, I dared to speak to the angel." The back of Nicolò's neck tingled. "I prayed for the future of my son, and the angel said my prayer was heard, that my Nicolò would become the world's greatest violinist." She spoke so softly now that they had to strain to hear her. "When I awoke I was on the floor, my hands bruised and scorched in several places."

They sat without speaking. As always, whenever his mother finished her story, no one could find his voice for a moment. At last, Germi said, softly, "Did the angel say that to become the world's greatest violinist, Nicolò should be locked in his room?"

His mother shook her head. "Germi, for shame!" A new expression in his friend's eyes told Nicolò that Germi had changed his mind. A while ago, he was relying on guile, trickery — anything he could think of to gain his objective. But now Germi, slightly shame-faced, stood up.

"At first," he told Nicolò's mother, "I didn't really want to hear the story. As you said, I know it well. I only wished to get your attention on something else." His face went crimson. "At the stalls in the square, one of us engages the shopkeeper's attention. We make him sad or glad or mad — it doesn't matter. Then it's easy to get away with an orange."

Nicolò giggled, but it didn't match the way he felt inside.

His mother said, "And it makes you happy, Germi, when you do that?"

"It's so funny!" Germi's lips spread in a wide grin. "Even when we're caught! The shopkeeper roars and shakes his fist. You should see him standing in the street, screaming himself hoarse." Nicolò couldn't meet his mother's glance. Germi frowned. "At least, I thought it was funny. . . ." He met her eyes unwaveringly. "But I couldn't do it to you! I tried — but I couldn't do it!"

Nicolò's heart applauded while it shriveled up. He'd break his word to Lisa! He imagined her waiting and watching the steps. Finally, she'd tell her father, "He didn't come and he said he would."

"It was wrong of me to ask you to disobey the master's orders," Germi said. Having begun his confession, he seemed eager to rid himself of its burden. "And I lied. I wanted you to belittle his authority! Then, I tried to frighten you by suggesting that the angel's promise would come to nothing if you didn't let Nicolò go free."

"I know, Germi." Her voice was low. "I know."

Nicolò gasped. So his mother had known all along! He studied her, wondering why he'd never noticed the quiet understanding in her tired face.

Germi rubbed the back of his leg with his other foot. "Nicolò, my friend." He smiled sheepishly. "I'm not much good to you, am I? I failed —"

Nicolò ran a hand through his curls. "But you tried, Germi. You're still the manager of Paganini!"

"But you didn't fail!" His mother stood up. Her eyes were dancing even as her voice rang with conviction. Conviction? This was another of her attributes that Nicolò had overlooked. "Now, you designing Italian gentlemen, listen to this!" she said. "Germi, you've won your client's release today in the only possible way you could ever have managed it. By being honest — truthful."

Nicolò let out a yell, threw his arms around Germi's neck. Grabbing his violin, he leapt to the door.

Germi beamed. *"Grazie, grazie."*

"Wait a minute. I'm not through yet." She looked at one, then the other. "This is the first and the last time I will do this. Understand? Nicolò?"

A dismaying thought struck him. She would have to take the consequences. He stammered, "Father —?"

She smiled. "I'll handle your father. This once. Remember. Just this once." She shooed them out of the door. "Now get on, both of you. Who ever heard of a virtuoso not appearing for his concert?"

5

They hurried down the worn steps, up the street, cut across the narrow alley toward the little passageway that would lead them directly into the square. Massive state buildings towered on each side. There wasn't room for two to walk abreast. Nicolo ran ahead of Germi. From the square they rushed down to the wharf. Nicolò's glance swept the audience scattered over the steps looking for a fair head. Please let her be here, he prayed silently. Don't let me be too late! Then he saw her, and everything in the whole world was exactly right. As they approached, she laughed aloud.

"*Bon jour! Buon giorno!* I knew you'd come. . . ."

Nicolò introduced Germi, saying, "I almost didn't get here. He handled it."

Germi exclaimed, "I almost didn't, too! Handle it, I mean."
Her silver-bell laughter sang in the air.

"You two aren't making any sense!"

Taking the violin from its case, placing the snuffbox in his
pocket, Nicolò defined the new partnership between Germi
and himself. Then he told her of their earlier predicament.
"I was afraid I'd miss you!" He paused. "In my room I
came to a conclusion — liberty and freedom are the best of
all things!"

A cloud passed over Lisa's face as she replied, "I'm glad
you're here."

The audience clapped noisily.

"Nicolò, we want our money back if there's not going to
be a concert!" They howled in merriment until Germi held
up a hand.

"The maestro is pleased to commence in a moment," he
announced. More laughter as he sat beside Lisa.

Something rubbed against his legs. Nicolò cried, "What
are you doing here? Following me around like a dog!" he
teased. He deposited Cat in Lisa's arms.

"Ummm." Lisa laid her cheek against the soft fur. "She's
pretty."

Nicolò was in perfect agreement. "She's pretty," he said.
"The sea's pretty, the day's pretty, you're pretty!"

"And you're pretty!" she added, matching his mood.

That brought Germi to his feet. "He's about as ugly as
he can get! Big nose, holes in his cheeks, skinny arms —"

"Beauty can be seen with the heart as well as the eyes,"
Lisa replied.

And even as he said lightly, "My ears — too much ears,"

59

Nicolò felt as if something had squeezed his heart quickly, and as quickly let it go. Lisa cuddled Cat, whose contented purring sounded like distant thunder. She said:

"The outside counts — but it's the inside that really shows."

Nicolò stepped out in front. He tapped the back of the violin with the stick of his bow. Now that he had a manager and this was a request performance, so to speak, a bit of formality was indicated. He waited for silence, tilting up his chin. Then he drew the bow. He played an aria, followed by *La Carmagnole,* with variations that popped into his head as he went along, for Lisa's benefit. A hymn that he'd written about his mother's dream, an étude, and at last, his imitations. With rapid bowing he went into a gavotte, its surprise ending exploding in *staccati.* All heads turned as one to the water and instantly back again. The jest was acknowledged in a spontaneous burst of applause.

"See? What did I tell you?" said the boy who had spoken the day before. "You thought it was the gulls!"

"Bravo! Encore!" They refused to move. "More, Nicolò, more!" Germi unwound himself and walked to Nicolo's side.

"Ladies and gentlemen —" He leaned over and scratched his big toe. "Ladies and gentlemen, the maestro thanks you — deeply — for this warm reception. However, he is very weary from his long journey through the Passo." There were gales of laughter. "And he wishes me to ask your indulgence. Besides —" he draped a hand on his hip bone — "you know it's time you were all getting home!"

They rose, stretched, sauntered off in different directions while Nicolò and Germi rejoined Lisa on the steps. During the concert, a beautiful little ship with gleaming white sails had come into the harbor. It didn't belong with the ponderous freight-carrying craft around it. Lisa said:

"Riding the waves as still as a lazy gull resting its wings."

Germi squinted. "Isn't that a rowboat being lowered over the side?" he asked. "And a ladder?"

"People —" Lisa shaded her eyes — "going down the ladder."

"Wonder who they are?" Nicolò said.

"Probably another duke, or earl, or baron—or king." Germi included everyone of importance except the clergy.

"What king?"

"What king? Any king! There are plenty — even if some of them can't keep up with their heads!"

And then Nicolò remembered something. He said to Lisa, "You spoke French a while ago. I thought you were from Leghorn."

"I am — now," she answered. "I was born in Paris. My mother was Italian. She died in the Revolution."

Nicolò winced. "I'm sorry," he said.

"If she had lived a little longer. . . . My father and I were helped to escape and we came to Leghorn where my mother's people are."

"Then your father is French?"

"Yes. He's Colonel Livron. He was artillery instructor for a time at the Military Academy in Paris."

Nicolò liked the way her lips moved as she talked, her wide forehead, winged brows. If he were an artist he doubted that he could paint all that he saw in her face. Taking his violin, he moved, quite suddenly, to the edge of the steps where a dusty magenta branch of bougainvillea tumbled from a low roof. His throat hurt as he contemplated the sea, the bumpy old rock that protruded from the water near the lighthouse. As he played a light tune, he watched the old rock change into a fig — an upside-down, fat, ripe, purple fig! The little ship became a toy in a bowl of blue water. As the last notes faded over the sea, he touched the branch and its trumpet-shaped flowers moving in the breeze were ballerinas, smiling, dipping, nodding. . . . He returned to Lisa's side. This morning, at home, he'd wanted to say something to her about beauty. Now he didn't know how to begin. She was laughing in response to a remark of Germi's and stroking Cat's head.

"You like her, don't you?" Nicolò said.

"Oh, yes!" She gave Cat a squeeze.

"Then I want you to have her!" He added, impulsively, "As a present from me."

"But I couldn't take her. She's yours!"

"My father doesn't like cats. He'll be glad I'm rid of her. Besides, uh — she's in the way. I've outgrown her." He rubbed Cat's head to let her know he didn't really mean it. It's better this way, Cat, his fingers said.

On their way home, after Lisa and her father had departed, Nicolò said, "Do you think I'm pretty, Germi?"

"Pretty!" Germi's eyebrows stood in points. "Nicolò, have you been bled, lately? You must be coming down with something!" He kicked a rotten tomato out of the way. "As I said once today, you're as pretty as a crazy eagle! Big beak, glittering eyes." He laughed, that funny expression surprising his face. "And when you frown, your mouth creases on each side like those *f* holes in the fiddle!"

Nicolò chuckled. Nobody but Germi could talk to him this way. He said, seriously, "I don't mean outside. She said it's the inside that shows. So beauty comes from inside, don't you see?"

"Sorta. . . ." Germi scratched his head. "You're speaking aesthetically."

"Aesthetic — what?"

"Artistically! You're an artist. You deal in feeling. I deal in facts. I'm a reasoner!" He may as well have said, "I am the Pope!" It was that powerful.

"What's a reasoner?"

"One who uses reason."

"What's reason?"

"Nicolò!" Germi fairly shouted it. He chose his next words, spacing them carefully, as though he were remembering a lesson as well as being enormously patient with his dull-witted friend. "Reason is a motive leading to an action, a cause that makes a fact, any fact, intelligible. Do you understand?"

"No."

"We are walking home, aren't we?"

"Of course!" It was Nicolò's turn to shout.

"That's the action, caused by the motive that we have to get home, that makes the fact that we will arrive at home intelligible. Get it?"

"It's a lot of words, all mixed up."

"It isn't mixed up. It's reason."

"Then I don't like it."

"How could you? You don't like anything but music."

"And from now on," Nicolò said firmly, "Paganini's music will come to life and endure."

"How?"

"Because I understand beauty — what and where it is. Do you want me to explain —" he laughed — "aesthetically?"

"I dare you!"

"We-ell. Beauty can speak without words. It lives in the heart, but it's everywhere." He grinned. "It doesn't need reason because it just *is!* It's invisible, too — yet always visible."

"Nicolò! And you have the nerve to say reason's all mixed up? You should listen to yourself. You're hopeless."

"Look!" Nicolò indicated the white-topped Ligurian Alps. "There's beauty!"

"If you like mountains." Germi shrugged. "Piles of earth and rock and snow!"

Nicolò slowed down, listening. A child was crying, low, plaintively. A mother's lullaby was caressing.

"There's beauty there, too," he said.

"In a baby crying for his supper?" Germi ran ahead. "Come on, Nicolò, I'll race you to the alley!"

6

Before the eighteenth century, women were forbidden by the Pope to perform on the stage. Consequently, all concerts were given by men. The favorite kind of singing was that of the *soprani castrati*, rare songsters, schooled with utmost care, their rooms kept far warmer than those of other students, to guard against their catching cold. Before mirrors, they practiced as long as fifteen hours a day to adapt body, mouth, even eyelids, in fitting gestures.

When the ruling was relaxed, the *castrati* then shared the principal roles with women singers, but the male soprano was still preferred. And although the Duchy of Genoa, republic of the Doges, would in a few years be replaced by Napoleon's new and more democratic regime, it was still possible for Marchesi, the most adored male soprano, to sail into the harbor of Genoa for a scheduled concert.

Sunday morning, as they dressed for Mass, the Paganinis talked about the impending event. The girls ran to and from the window, delighted at the sight of the quaint craft sparkling in the early sunlight.

"Every seat in the theater will be taken!" Nicolò's mother said. She had amazed Nicolò by the way she had handled his father yesterday. Antonio had not been the least disturbed when she disobeyed his orders. On the contrary, he was jovial.

"It's said his protector is a cardinal of Rome," the master informed his family. "He's given the singer palaces, villas, gifts." He laughed. "The audience can have his voice. I'll take the box-office receipts!"

Carlo, at the pump, yawned sleepily. He touched water to his face, drying it immediately. His Sunday bath concluded, he said, "Has anybody seen my stockings?"

At last they were ready, and they set off through the narrow quarter, up the hill to San Lorenzo. Other worshipers were in the streets; men in their best suits, women mostly in somber black. Germi joined them, moved in beside Nicolò as the girls ran ahead. Behind, Carlo walked with his parents.

Glancing over his shoulder, Nicolò said, in an undertone, "Don't mention our pact. My father sees himself as my manager and now isn't the time for him to find out he's not."

"Logically, since he must be told, why wait?" Germi laughed. "But the wish to avoid his anger makes the fact that I'm glad to say nothing — intelligible!" Germi was baiting him! Nicolò couldn't think of a retort.

"Music is easier," he replied honestly. They had almost reached the Duomo, when he stooped to unbend the sole of his shoe. It had ripped back and, with every step, folded under his arch. It was like walking on a hard sausage. He didn't see who had passed, but there was a flurry of whisperings, a tremor of excitement in the group around him. From his crouched position, he asked, "Who was that?"

"He's important, whoever he is," Germi replied. "Walks with his head up, wears an embroidered yellow waistcoat—"

Nicolò stood, straining to see, but the stranger had already entered the church. As Nicolò entered, too, the smell of incense, the scent of arum and Madonna lilies was heavy. His glance rested a moment on the sad, sweet face of the *Pietà*, passed the chapel of John the Baptist, rose to the vaulted dome, still higher to a stained-glass lunette whose figures shone scarlet and blue in the sun's rays. . . . Now he knew what she meant! This morning, he did feel beautiful inside.

In this frame of mind, during the celebration of the Grand Mass, at an imperceptible nod from Signor Costa, he stepped to the raised stand, looked into the multitude of upturned faces and deliberately drew his bow. The sacred concert pouring from organs, violas, violoncellos, flooded the Cathedral. During the *soli* Nicolò ran his fingers up and down the strings with hardly a thought to the notes. He played from his heart.

The worshipers sat spellbound. Some of them openly

wept. Just below him, a man in a yellow waistcoast rose from his seat. Wearing the blank stare of a sleepwalker, he gazed at Nicolò in an hypnotic trance. Then he crossed himself and hurried from the church.

An hour later, when Nicolò and Germi returned to the Paganini house, Nicolò had forgotten the incident — until he saw the stranger standing squarely in the middle of the room! The man was speaking to the family who were ringed around him.

"And I said to myself, I'll find him if I have to search every house in Genoa!"

Nicolò's sister, Domenicia, giggled.

"Did you?" Her eyes were big. "Search every house for my brother?"

"Come in, son!" Antonio Paganini urged, seeing him at the door. "You and Germi." Nicolò put his violin on the table. Something was afoot. His father was behaving decently.

His mother stammered, "Th — this is —"

"Signor Luigi Marchesi!" Antonio announced, showing all his teeth.

Marchesi? Nicolò thought, astonished. Here — in his home? "How do you do, sir!" he said. The waistcoat was very elegant at close range. Embroidered all over, and butter-colored, the color of Lisa's hair.

Carlo nudged his elbow, whispering: "He's wearing perfume! And look at his hands!"

Marchesi blew a kiss from tapered fingers, their nails filed to points.

"Ah, what a genius!" he said. "In your music is heaven. I was overcome in church this morning. I had to leave!"

"Thank you, sir. I thought I played well, also."

Marchesi laughed in a high treble, including them in a burst of confidence. "I told friends the heavy incense overpowered me!"

Nicolò stole a glance at Germi and knew that he was thinking the same thing. Marchesi wouldn't be wasting time coming here just to praise. What. . . .

"Signor, sit here." Antonio fluffed a cushion, said to his wife, "Bring wine!"

Marchesi demurred. "To get to the purpose of my visit: La Bertionetti and I, we're on tour." As if all of Genoa didn't know! "We sing at Teatro Sant 'Agostino on Tuesday next." He addressed Nicolò. "And you, demon of the violin, will you do us the honor of performing with us?"

"In concert?" Nicolò's legs went limp. He had to sit down.

Antonio squeezed himself between Nicolò and the singer. "It's most satisfying," he said, "to hear my son's ability extolled. I've worked hard to perfect his talent. Now — as to remuneration, I handle my son's financial arrangements."

Marchesi's face was pink above his collar; tiny beads of perspiration shone on his temples. "On the way from Bologna," he told them, "the novel idea occurred to me — to us — to use local talent in our concert." Staring at a spot just above Antonio's head, he added, "However, there was no thought of compensation." He picked a speck from his coat sleeve. "Genoa will have the opportunity of hearing its prodigy, and, after all, the privilege of appearing with Marchesi."

"Indeed, sir!" Nicolò's mother told the singer. "You have made our hearts proud!"

Nicolò was phrasing his reply carefully in his mind.

69

"You can't buy shoes with a proud heart!" Antonio sputtered. "The word 'free' makes me feel sick. He gives free concerts on the wharf, plays for free in the Cathedral. Now you come here asking him to play for free at the theater! Will he go to his grave playing for free?"

Marchesi made a motion with delicate fingers. "I have made a mistake," he murmured, and moved toward the door. "I do not wish to be insulted further."

"Sir!" Nicolò rose. "You haven't asked my opinion, yet this concerns me!"

Marchesi swung around. "You're only a boy! I thought —"

"And you thought right!" Antonio interrupted. "He never makes a move without my consent!"

"Let him have his say," his mother pleaded.

"I intend to." Nicolò sent a warning glance around the room before he spoke. "Signor, I appreciate your compliments. However, you've overlooked something. If — *if* — I perform with the great Marchesi, he too will benefit." Marchesi squealed in merriment.

"How do you figure that? You're a nobody!"

Nicolò was glad the singer was amused. He himself was abashed by his own effrontery. Nevertheless, it was how he felt.

"No," he said. "I am not a nobody. I am a Paganini! Soon to become the world's greatest violinist. What could be more exciting? Marchesi and Paganini, on the same bill!"

Marchesi executed a little dance step. "Then you will?"

"I will!"

"I forbid it!" Antonio shook his fist. "Nicolò, demand your rights — your *pay!* Your backbone is cold spaghetti!"

Marchesi looked from one to the other. It was clear that he wanted no part of a family row. He edged to the door.

Nicolò read a message in Germi's eyes. Quickly, he asked what he had in mind.

"I thought we could walk a way with the signor," Germi told him. He winked at Nicolò as they descended to the street, where a peddler atop a pile of rags in a cart behind a donkey warbled an aria. Nicolò, lighthearted, stopped before the Madonna to say a prayer of thanks for Germi, who had taken over his responsibilities. Crossing himself, he then ran to join Marchesi and Germi at the corner. Because his friend was explaining their partnership, Nicolò remained silent. "And therefore, Signor," Germi was saying, "I propose a plan." Marchesi picked his way, selecting the cleanest places for his feet.

"A plan?" he said.

"Suppose Nicolò accepts your invitation with a reciprocal courtesy. That is to say, if, at his formal debut, *you* will be *his* guest?" Marchesi's eyes opened wide.

"You are quite a manager! If you ever decide to take on another client —" He turned to Nicolò, "When is your debut?"

"I — er —" Nicolò pushed his tongue to the roof of his mouth. He'd nearly said, "I've no idea!"

Germi rushed in. "Shortly," he lied. "Perhaps in July."

July? Nicolò's pulse quickened. A formal debut? Germi read his thoughts and shrugged as if to say, why not? July's a good month. Nicolò put his hands in his pockets, crossed his hidden fingers. They went under the Porto Soprano, crossed to the square. The stalls were closed now, grillwork criss-crossing their faces. Papers eddied in the breeze that scattered yesterday's dead petals from the flower bins. Marchesi fell into step beside him.

"You said, back there, that you will become the world's greatest violinist. There's no doubt?"

Nicolò hitched up his trousers. "That is correct," he assured him. "No, there's no doubt." The wind had changed. It blew from the water. The salty, tangy scent was pleasant after Marchesi's heavy perfume. With a twinkle in his eye, the singer said:

"I'd hate to think that I muffed the opportunity of performing with the world-renowned Paganini! Sir," he told Germi, "it's a deal. I accept your terms."

Germi's eyes crinkled. "How can I get in touch with you? When the time comes?"

"Just send a message to my quarters in Bologna," Marchesi replied. "In Borgo Spesso, second alley up, first door to the right in the Saint Mario section." He confided, "Named after the patron saint of our church."

"I'll play my variations, Tuesday next," Nicolò announced. "And the Silver Étude." They shook hands all around.

"The Silver Étude?" Marchesi asked. "A new composition?"

"It will be," Nicolò replied. "You see, I haven't written it yet."

Marchesi's mouth opened wide, like a fish too long out of water. But all he said was, "Rehearsal, tomorrow, at the theater." He walked jauntily down the street away from them.

Nicolò took his hands from his pockets, uncrossed his

fingers. With a smile he said to Germi, "Get set!" He placed a foot ahead. "I'll race you home."

7

That evening, Nicolò wrote the Silver Étude. It danced itself through his head with such intensity, during supper, that he paid scant attention to the family's animated conversation about his imminent concert with Marchesi, as well as Germi's new role. He was aware, however, that his father raged in a manner different from his usual behavior. Instead of resorting to a tirade, Antonio, a wounded bear, crept into a cave of gloomy silence as he suffered because of his son's new assertiveness. Nicolò understood. To lose face was the most detestable of all things. Since his father viewed the partnership as a childish game, and considered the plan to participate in a formal concert without pay, regardless of the honor, as idiocy, Nicolò wasn't surprised when he finally mumbled:

"There are some who fiddle their days away and the

fiddling amounts to nothing. Others are proclaimed as 'geniuses' — but what good does it do!" Fixing Nicolò with a studied stare, he lamented, "Trying to get something into your head is like trying to color the Bay with chianti! The labor's lost and so's the wine!"

Unable to think of a suitable reply, Nicolò left the table. In his room he arranged quill, paper, ink. He ruled the staffs down the pages, set the key signatures. The quill moved rapidly, spewing black notes over the pages. He paused at intervals, to pluck the strings of his violin, depress, listen, before he resumed writing. The melody would be carried by the bow. At the same time, his left hand would execute a *pizzicato* accompaniment.

At length, laying aside the pen, he crossed to the window and stood with arms folded to watch the purple-shadowed surf pounding heavily. The idea hit him all of a sudden. The sound waves from his violin were like those large billows out there, with little ripples on them, perhaps tinier ripples on the little ripples, if his eyes could see. Then all valuable sounds in music were also made up of mixed waves! The main wave was the tone, and all the others that went with it were the overtones or harmonics. And the string made them all — the main wave itself and also the little waves and ripples!

He reached the table in a leap and scanned the new composition. Striking out passages here and there, he inserted groups of notes that would produce this exciting overlapping. He smiled as he worked, delighted with this new discovery which was touched with the same mysterious light that sparkled phosphorescent in the surf. He was unaware that anyone had entered the room until he heard breathing at his shoulder. He whirled in quick alarm. His father's lips were a thin line.

"Not a sound from this room in over an hour!" he said. "Nicolò, if you're wasting your time, I'll —"

"Look!" Nicolò pointed. "I'm writing a new étude."

"Frantic notes! Skipping, jumping, flying!" His father's voice was scornful. "Resembles a cat-and-dog fight more than anything else. Nicolò, why aren't you practicing this new piece?"

"I am, Father. In my head. It isn't right yet."

"How do you know? What nonsense are you speaking now?"

"I want to finish it up here first." Nicolò touched his forehead. Before his father could reply, he put the violin under his chin. Using the only weapon he knew to placate his father, he began a staccato study, running his fingers up and down the keyboard with tremendous speed. With the last fortissimo chord, he dropped his arm, letting the blood circulate normally again.

Antonio said, "Seems I've heard that before, yet now it's different." The bed springs creaked under his father's weight.

"It is!" Nicolò leaned a knee on the chair. "I added my own variations."

"Musical gymnastics!" Antonio's voice sharpened. "Why must you always go off half-cocked, adding trills and frills and rills —"

"Because that makes it mine!" Nicolò remembered something and moved back his chair.

"Where are you going?" Antonio was on his feet with surprising agility.

"To find hot water."

"Hot water? Hot water's to wash for Mass!" Nevertheless, he followed close behind and watched silently as Nicolò found warm water on the stove and plunged his hand into the pot. "Holy Saints, Nicolò, since when did you take such a liking to cleanliness?"

"I'm not washing my hand, Father. I'm soaking it, to make it limber. To develop the breadth and stretch of the fingers. I noticed a while ago. . . ."

Antonio struck his forehead with his open palm. Not waiting to hear what Nicolò had noticed, he said flatly, "There've been Paganinis in Italy as long as there've been olive trees. All kinds of Paganinis! One, Carro, was a canon. There was Giovanni, the priest, and another who ran away and lived on berries in the hills. And your grandfather, God rest his soul, who carried a snuffbox for fifty years to bring him good luck." Antonio scratched his chin. "Yes, we've had some queer ones along the way, but never before now have we ever had a noodle!" Hunching his shoulders, he turned around and walked away from the stove.

Later, much later, back in his room where he'd worked late into the night, Nicolò at last was ready to run through Lisa's Silver Étude. It was necessarily a brief composition with a melody so simple anybody could hum it, but the tracery of accompaniment, the little waves and ripples that ran in and out, was the part that he'd wanted so badly to capture, and he had. At its conclusion, he dropped the bow and sat down, pleased with himself. The string made the main wave and also the little waves and ripples. *The* string? *One* string? Was it possible to play on a single string? His fingers flew to the pegs, releasing all but the G. Held only at the tailpiece, the other three slid over, dangling above the floor like cooked spaghetti. In a fever of enthusiasm Nicolò was plucking, depressing, shortening and lengthening the vibration when his father entered the room for the second time.

"Was that a new étude?" He saw the strings. "At this time of night?" he questioned. Puzzled, he came closer. "What are you doing?" He stared, mingled incredulity and astonishment in his eyes, then backed out of the room. "Theresa, Theresa!" he yelled.

Nicolò, dropping the violin, followed him. "Father! I can explain!" He tried to keep his voice down. There was no need to wake the whole house.

Antonio thought differently. He was informing the neighborhood, "I thought he was changing the strings! But he's gone mad! Saints preserve us, Nicolò's tearing up his fiddle!"

His mother and Carlo almost collided at the door. Their vacant, vapid stares belonged to persons awakened too suddenly from sleep. The girls, in their nightgowns, huddled together.

"I'm doing no such thing!" Nicolò stormed. He grew angrier by the second. "I was only experimenting with one string."

A vein stood out in his father's temple. "Sit down!" Antonio said. At the sight of his face, the girls raced back to their beds. Antonio informed the others, "What I saw in there has made up my mind! You need another teacher,

79

Nicolò. You've outgrown everybody here. You waste half your time dreaming up difficulties and the other half dreaming up difficulties for those difficulties!" He cleared his throat. "There's a Maestro Allessandro Rolla in Parma —" At his wife's raised eyebrows, he nodded. "I've inquired around. This Rolla is the pride of Italy." He smiled thinly. "He doesn't take many pupils, but he'll take Nicolò! So . . . I've decided to place my son in the hands of this distinguished artist."

Professor Rolla! Nicolò caught his breath. Parma! A thrill of pleasure shook him. The outside world — a new adventure, a new life. . . . His heart thudded to his feet.

"But Germi lives here!" he said, thinking he could not leave his best friend, his manager, behind.

"When?" His mother choked on the word.

"Soon!" His father leaned back in his chair. "I have a little money put aside. That, with what I'll win in the lottery. I'm sure, this time, I hold the lucky combination!" Nicolò bit his lip, hard. Antonio slapped his thigh. "It's all settled," he said. "We go to Parma!" Nicolò lowered his glance to the floor. This must be how a fish felt as the net was hauled in — flapping and flipping, getting more and more tangled up. . . .

"Well, Nicolò, aren't you pleased? To look at you, anyone would think I'd asked you to take a bath or something!"

His mother stammered, "I'm certain Nicolò appreciates —"

"His face is in mourning because he's so happy?"

Nicolò raised his eyes. "Father, I am excited at the thought of Professor Rolla. I am grateful to you. It's just that —"

80

"Act like it, then!" Antonio said. "Show some appreciation!"

"Father —" he began again. "Thank you, sir. . . ." What would life be worth without Germi? He stumbled from the room.

In bed, he stared at the dark. There was no moon, and he was glad. The night matched his black despair. How did you say good-bye to your best friend? How was he going to tell Germi? Nicolò turned over on his stomach. Well, he wouldn't! Not yet. He'd put if off as long as he could!

Occupied during the next two days with rehearsals, lessons from Costa, and further work on the étude, Nicolò didn't stop to think, until later, that Germi was deliberately avoiding him. In fact, his mother unwittingly brought it to his attention. She had procured a length of black velvet and rushed to complete new trousers for his performance.

"Stand still," she said on Tuesday, after she'd promised that this was the last fitting. "Let me look at you. Tonight, I won't see anything!" Nicolò ran his hand over the fabric. It was soft — soft and smooth and silken. "Ah!" Her eyes glowed. "My beautiful Nicolò! Take them off. They're finished!" Then she added, "Where's Germi? I miss him."

A feather of uneasiness fluttered in his chest. "Oh, he'll be along," he said in an off-hand way, but to convince himself, he went to the window and searched the street, realizing that the very last time he'd seen his friend was on Sunday, when they'd raced home after bidding Marchesi good-bye. This was unlike Germi. Suppose he were ill? No, Nicolò dismissed the thought instantly. Germi was never sick. . . .

Now that he really put his mind to it, he did recall seeing Germi from a short distance, yesterday, as he walked to Costa's. His friend had behaved oddly, although it had made no impression at the time. Nicolò now remembered how Germi, as usual, had waited at the end of the street. Then, when Nicolò was almost up to him, he had turned, and run out of sight, between the buildings.

Nicolò had to admit that he was glad that Germi's action made it impossible to discuss Parma, but Germi couldn't know any of this, so why was he acting in such a manner? Nicolò left the window. Now he was worried.

Six hours later, when Germi joined Nicolò at the theater, he appeared to be his normal self. And that was just it. He only *appeared* so. Something lurked in his eyes. Upon entering the musty green room backstage where Nicolò waited, he grinned, but the odd expression didn't quite come off.

Nicolò's anxiety was sharp and uncomfortable. "Where've you been?" he asked. "And why did you run from the corner yesterday?"

"Corner? Run? What corner?" Germi's glance ricocheted along the far wall. Nicolò didn't reply. The last thing in the world he wanted at this time was an argument. He didn't feel well. And all that mad confusion on the other side of the closed door wasn't helping. Flustered stagehands issuing orders above discordant scrapings of instruments in final tuning, prompters lamenting misplaced scripts, the haste of last-minute roulades by Marchesi and La Bertionetti, at the clavier. . . . Somebody stumbled, let out a curse. And no wonder, thought Nicolo, visualizing the wretched candle ends sputtering in wooden sconces that illuminated the stage. The oval hall was dark except for a dim light in the boxes of the nobility and the evil-smelling tallow candles lighting the orchestra until the performance began. Their odor was thick and overpowering. He wiped sweat from his forehead, tried to laugh.

"Germi," he said finally, "I — I think I'm scared." He held his stomach. "It's full of rocks." Saliva gushed into his mouth. "Where's a basin? I'm going to be sick —"

"No, you're not!" Germi smacked him square in the face. "*Ow!*"

"You're going out there and play like a Paganini! Furthermore, before you're through, you'll silence the pit!" Nicolò rubbed his face. The rocks melted and flowed together in a layer of confidence. He examined his shoe.

"I'll silence them," he said. "If I can get out there on this sausage."

"Here, put your foot on this chair." Germi pulled out his knife. "I'll cut off the sole of your shoe!"

"Then it won't have a bottom."

"So what? Who'll know what you're walking on?" Germi sliced the sole. "See if that's better."

Nicolò giggled. "The floor's cold!"

His mother came in, cried, and straightened his frill. She kissed him, saying, "Carlo, Domenicia, Nicoletta — they're all out there! Your family is proud of you!" She was saying that his father was proud, also, even though he couldn't show it. Antonio, preferring to remain at home, had announced earlier, "I'll be present, near the box office, at a performance when receipts are to be counted!" She smoothed a curl, adjusted a sleeve, and finally made her way out.

Increasing racket indicated that the pit was rapidly filling with "rabble," the term used to isolate those members of society whom the patricians considered inferior to themselves.

"Let's sneak outside and watch," Germi said. Nicolò tuned his violin, rosined up his bow, transferred the snuff-box to his pocket. "Keep it with you," his grandfather had said. "It will always bring good luck." Lord, how he hoped this was true! He followed Germi to a vantage point in the wings.

When Bertinetti, in eloquent voice and extravagant costume, made her entrance, the audience hissed to remind her that she could never usurp the place of their favorite male soprano. Unperturbed, she sang to them, and Nicolò agreed with those who called her a nightingale. As he listened, he surveyed the ancient Sant 'Agostino, which was filled tonight; all five tiers, with boxes, plus the pit where spectators coughed and crowded together. Some were eating and laughing merrily. Others carried long sticks with which to pound the benches. In the amphitheater, servants watched their masters in the boxes above. If signaled, they lighted lanterns on the spot and escorted the noblesse outside, to waiting carriages. Several elegant gentlemen seated around a table in the royal box on the second level gambled at cards. The ladies wore pale blonde wigs combed high, adorned with pins of gold filigree, with saucy curls across the forehead, a long tress to the shoulder. Gowns sparkled and shone in every color. As they chatted gaily, the ladies rattled their favorite trinkets; boxes containing smelling salts, cases for beauty spots. Nicolò was sure their delicate hands had never touched a stove. He forced his attention on the box itself. Mirrored, the far side reflected the performance for the gamblers with their backs to the stage. Nicolò studied the spectacle with mounting irritation.

"Germi," he said, "is there anyone who came to listen?"

"They are listening!" Germi replied. "And gossiping, flirting, being seen — and gambling. Most of them love the opera and know it as well as the singer." He laughed. "If you think this is noisy, wait until Marchesi shows up!"

As though his word were the cue, from Bertionetti's throat soared the ornamental flight of the cadenza. Even as applause shook the house, a fanfare of trumpets blasted the air. Nicolò grabbed his ears as Marchesi loomed on the ramp in a full suit of armor — plumed helmet, sword, shield, and lance. The crowd went insane. The pit clapped, whistled, shrieked, as sticks rained blow after blow on the benches. Printed sonnets, praising the singer, fluttered from the boxes, and this caused scuffling in the pit. Marchesi received these delirious tributes with a smile and launched into his own favorite aria — from a different opera! He sang on and on, acclaimed all the time he was singing, in a fantastic uproar. Nicolò pressed his ears tighter and stared. At the footlights, Marchesi, rolling his heavily made-up eyes, motioned to the audience, talked to the prompter in the wings, even kept time to the music with his sword. Then, discarding his splendid armor, he unfastened the neck of his blouse. He took snuff and kicked off his slippers.

Nicolò exclaimed, "He'll be half naked by the time he's done!"

"In a minute, now." Germi gave a little push. "You're next." Nicolò's middle was warm water sloshing against his ribs. His legs wouldn't move. Then his hand closed over the snuffbox in his pocket. With a toss of his curls he walked onto the stage.

Howls and cries rose anew. He was surrounded by jeering, laughing faces, noise, indifference, offending gamblers. What a contrast to the wharf audience! For the first time in his life, Nicolò felt completely alone. Breathing through pinched nostrils, he thought he would stand there forever before he could make a sound. The din grew louder; endless bursts of laughter interspersed with high voices and low voices, whisperings, sneezes, outcries of every kind. Blood drained from his face. His lips were stiff as parchment. He would defy anyone, from peddlers to kings, for this insult to music! The orchestra finished the introduction, the music diminished. . . .

Nicolò looked straight ahead. Then arching his wrist, he let the bow fall on the E string. *Staccati* erupted from the little Amati as though his wrist were impelled by a spring of taut steel. His variations were shooting stars diving into the darkness. Laughter broke off in the throats. Several persons left the benches and stood gaping. The noise dimmed to a hum. Without stopping, he moved into the Silver Étude. His *legato* bowing in thirds and then sixths expressed the beautiful singing tone of Lisa's laughter. A stick clattered to the floor unheeded. He played on and on, in full swing, remembering Servetto's advice: "Don't

raise the fingers on one string before the tone of the next string sounds." The voice of his violin at times seemed to stop singing and whispered before rising again in glorious song. Their cards forgotten, the gamblers turned to face him. No one coughed, no one sneezed, no one moved. In rich, sweet melody he continued to the very end. With a sudden last pluck of the strings, he dropped the bow.

There wasn't a sound. Then — hysterical, tumultuous applause! Nicolò smiled and bowed, gathering the moment to him. He bowed and smiled. This golden moment of hands that clapped, eyes that praised, hearts that loved! Then he turned and ran toward Germi.

"Bravo!" Germi's eyes were swimming. "Bravo!" People milled about, all talking at once. His mother and sisters pushed forward. Marchesi motioned above the heads of the crowd and hurried out, trailing the familiar perfume.

A giant of a person was bearing down from the right. He was good-looking, with a remarkable black moustache riding at full sail on his upper lip. His correct *velada,* over a flowered silk waistcoat, was wide open across the chest, with large side pockets. The embroidered front glistened with stones of cut glass. He carried a large muff for his cards and money. Directing Germi's attention, Nicolò said, "Who's that?"

Germi watched the oncoming gentleman with interest. He was speaking excitedly to a friend at his side.

"— magic-fingered boy genius!" he concluded. At that instant Nicolò was lifted off his feet, held high in the air. The stranger kissed him soundly on both his hot cheeks and shouted, "Tonight, you've proved that God lives in

every man! You are divine! Come to my house tomorrow!"
Nicolò's feet touched the floor again and the stranger
melted into the crowd.

"Come to his house!" Nicolò exclaimed. "I don't even
know who he is!"

Someone said, "He doesn't do that often!" Another
volunteered, "Marquis Gian Carlo di Negro, Genoa's rising
patron of the arts. They say his name is inscribed in the
Book of Gold! That it cost ten thousand livres. The knives
and forks at his table are used once, then they are thrown
into the sea!"

Nicolò knew that he was standing in the center of a
dream. Any minute, now, he'd wake up. The feeling persisted as he joined his happy family at the stage door, and
together they moved out into the street.

8

Di Negro's marble villa snuggled into the hillside like a pink shell washed up by the sea. Waiting in the colossal hall, Nicolò was faced by the impersonal, penetrating stares from ancestral portraits. He was glad he'd worn clean linen and shoes, although one was minus a sole. The elderly manservant returned, led him down a corridor into a room that was furnished with elaborate consoles and gilded armchairs and was much larger than his entire house. Surely, the Colosseum at Rome could be no larger! Books lined one wall to the ceiling. Heavy velvet draperies obscured the sunlight. At first Nicolò thought he was alone. He stood, ill at ease, as the door closed behind him.

"Paganini?" The Marquis, unfolding himself from an armchair, rose behind a desk as broad and forbidding as the stage on which Nicolò had performed the night before. In modest black attire, his host seemed even taller than Nicolò remembered. "Come in, come in!" He strode to the windows, parted the draperies. "We can't talk in the dark!" Looking at Nicolò for the first time, he laughed aloud. "Don't let all this overwhelm you!" He gestured. "This monstrosity belongs to my uncle. He has millions because he never spends anything. Half the place is closed off." His moustache shone as if it had been oiled. "That poor soul, Alberto, who let you in, is our entire staff. Of course," he went on, "all of that will have to be changed!"

Nicolò's timidity vanished. "If you don't like it, why do you live here?"

"Getting to the heart at once, aren't you? Discarding the outer layers, proceeding to the core — like eating an artichoke!" The Marquis thought this amusing. "Yes," he said, "we are going to get along famously!" They took chairs. Di Negro stretched out his long legs and said, "I am a poet."

"A good one?" Nicolò added matter-of-factly. "Anyone can be mediocre."

"My work isn't mediocre!" Di Negro laughed. "If anything, it's a bit — er — flamboyant. My uncle has taken me into his house to shelter me from certain further — er — restraints and limitations which I suffered from the police. . . ."

"Police?" Nicolò sat upright.

"At the injunction of Rome." His handsome face was regretful.

"I'd like to see anyone try to restrict the kind of music I compose," Nicolò said fiercely.

The Marquis didn't pursue the subject. He said, "I'll bring this place back to life! And that's why I asked you here today."

"Me? What does it have to do with me?"

"Ah!" Di Negro squirmed in his chair. "You see," he said, "I have everything that money can provide except. . . ." He flashed a smile. Nicolò wasn't fooled. Whatever he had to say was costing great effort. "Oh, I've pocket money, of course," Di Negro went on, "and I manage to pick up some at the tables, but I can't attach you as chamber virtuoso with financial reward." His face was pink. "I can't pay you!"

"Pay me for what?"

"For performing here, in the salon. Playing for my friends, at parties, dinners. Will you?"

"You can find a fiddler anywhere, any time!"

"I don't want a fiddler! I want Paganini!" All of us, Nicolò thought, watching Di Negro, all Italians use their hands as soft or loud pedals. "There's little I can offer in return." Di Negro's voice trailed off. Little? That would depend on one's definition.

Nicolò crossed one foot over the other. He said. "We've always been poor. Poverty has turned my father's heart to rock, cut lines in my mother's face. Poverty is squeezing the love out of our family." Di Negro lowered his eyelids. An odd expression ran over his face, disappearing at once. Nicolò resumed. "Many times I've seen myself in fine clothes, moving in beautiful places, like this house . . . but, first, I must learn how." He asked shyly, "Did you ever go to school?"

"The College of San Carlo."

"Do you know that I can read or write hardly at all?"

"Do you know that I don't even know how to pick up a violin?" The Marquis wasn't only tall. He was big — big clear through.

"Though — education is not exactly what I mean." Nicolò stopped, not knowing how to proceed.

"Social grace." Di Negro leaned forward. "For lack of a better word, shall we say, 'polish'?"

"Polish!" Nicolò laughed. "All right," he bargained, "I'll play for your friends if you'll polish me, make me shine! Not only on the outside — on the inside, too. That's belonging to somebody and having them belong to you!" He stopped, embarrassed. Di Negro eyed the door.

"I'm ravenous!" he said. "I took the liberty of assuming you'd have lunch with me." Alberto came in, with a silver platter, a slim bottle of wine. There were little pigeons in butter, thin veal tossed in oil, odd dishes which Nicolò had never tasted before, and cool slices of pumpkin.

Later, as he was about to leave, the Marquis said, "One more favor. I wonder if you'd swap me your shoes for a new pair?" Nicolò clenched his fists. Blood threatened to break a vein in his neck. Back there, in the library, he hadn't been careful enough. The Marquis had seen his bare foot! Di Negro added, deliberately, "Last night, sir, I beheld genius of the highest order. I want a memento of that occasion, so I can say, 'I own the shoes that Paganini wore

the night I first heard him —' You wouldn't deny me that pleasure?" The moustache trembled ever so slightly. Nicolò met his eyes without a waver.

"If that's the truth," he said, "I'd be honored to give you the shoes. But a Paganini never accepts charity!"

"Charity?" The Marquis smiled. "I am in your debt for the rest of my life. Today I have met a man! May I shake the hand of Paganini?"

Nicolò's slender fingers were lost in the big palm. He stood erect. The Marquis had called him "sir," had asked permission to shake his hand! He walked away from the villa without even touching the ground.

At the square, awnings covered the stalls. Shopkeepers had returned home for the *riposo,* afternoon nap. Nicolò began to run, loping past the Columbus house, under the Porto Soprano, down a steep stairway, up the other side and *wham!* — collided head-on with Germi!

"Somebody chasing you, Nicolò?" Germi screwed up his face. "Where've you been? I looked all over!"

"To lunch with the Marquis!"

"Wow! What did you talk about?"

"Polish. Now let's hear you reason that out!"

"I have something to tell you —"

"Not until you hear what I've got to say!" Nicolò recounted the morning. "You'll like Di Negro," he said. "You're going with me, next time."

"Soon, I hope!"

"Of course, soon! I don't know how much —" He broke off just in time. He'd almost said, "I don't know how much longer I'll be in Genoa."

"How much — what?" Germi's face was wooden.

"Uh — er — time there'll be before the first musicale —"
It made no sense whatsoever, but it would have to do. It
was all he could think of. He looked away from Germi.

"Nicolò, when you look like that, you're up to something.
What is it?"

"I told you that I would dine with princes — well, he's
almost a prince — and conquer the world. That's what I'm
up to! I'm on my way home to prepare my weapons. To
practice, my friend!"

At daybreak, he jumped wide awake. Yesterday, Germi
had wanted to say something. He'd meant to ask about it
later, but in his own excitement had forgotten. Throwing
on his clothes, he slipped out of the house, hurried down
the stone steps. Before the little Madonna, he crossed
himself.

"Oh, blessed Mother," he prayed, "don't let my father
win in the lottery. As anxious as I am to go to Parma, I
mustn't leave Germi when there's something wrong with
him." The bell in the Duomo sounded, its tone rolling out
to sea where the gulls invaded it with their scratchy cries.
Germi wouldn't be up and about yet. It was too early.
Nicolò entered the narrow passageway. He could kill time
at the square, but he wasn't in the mood for the voices,
the haggling, the bustling. Turning around, he went behind
the state buildings in a short cut down to the steps. Noises
were beginning at the dock, bright washings marched out
on the clotheslines. The Marquis was probably just awaken-

ing in a great bed with silk sheets, a pot of chocolate on the table beside him.

Nicolò exclaimed, "Good morning, sir!" Quickly turning his head, he made his mouth into a snout to hold a leaf spray.

"Why, good morning, Nicolò!" He imitated Di Negro's voice and handed a cup of chocolate to the air. "Have this! There's *biscotti* — cookies. *Mangiate bene!* Eat well!" Nicolò flipped the spray behind his back. In his own voice, he said:

"No, thank you, I'm not hungry." The spray went above the snout again.

"Nonsense. There are cherries, figs. Eat up! We'll just throw what's left into the sea!"

"Nicolò" Germi's voice was inches behind his ear. "What's ailing you? Who do you think you're talking to?"

"Germi —" Nicolò held back his grin — "may I present the Marquis Carlo Di Negro? He's having his breakfast in bed."

"How do you do?" Germi leaned over the steps, his shoulders shaking with glee. "Your foot, sir, is out of the covers!" He rearranged the bedclothes. Nicolò snickered but kept to Di Negro's voice.

"A fig? Cookies?" Laughter spread his snout, the spray fell to the ground. Giggling, they darted into an alley, unmindful of the drippings overhead. Nicolò said, "I was waiting. Didn't think you'd be up so early."

"I couldn't sleep."

"Why?"

"How do I know? I couldn't sleep, that's all. Do I have to have a reason?" Germi pulled a twig from a crack in the wall and leaned back, chewing the stem.

"Do you have to have a reason? When you're the most reasoning reasoner there is?" Nicolò spread his hands wide on the wall at Germi's shoulders. "Of course you do. What is it?" Germi tried to wriggle away. But Nicolò held fast. "For two or three days, you've been acting funny," he said. "Don't pretend you haven't." Germi threw away the twig. "Move your arms, Nicolò," he said. "I'll tell you. . . . You know how it is on a winter's morning when there's no hot water? You can't find the courage to wash. Then, all of a sudden, you take a deep breath and stick your whole head under the pump?"

"Yes?"

"Well —" He gulped. "I'm leaving Genoa next month. To enter the University at Parma."

"Parma?" A bundle of hot wires exploded in his stomach. Nicolò jumped high in the air and burst into tears. Germi turned his back. Nicolò spun him around. "Wait," he said, "don't cry!"

"Well, *you* are!" A tear ran down and Germi caught it with his tongue. "No! I mean, yes, but it isn't really crying! Germi — I'm leaving Genoa, too — to study in Parma!"

Germi let out a yell you could hear all the way up to San Lorenzo. Nicolò ran up the alley, improvising a tune. "We're soon to take a trip, we're soon to go away."

Germi's singsong voice chimed in, "Get up, everybody, and celebrate today!"

Nicolò urged, "Onward! We're calling on the Marquis!"

They raced out of the Passo, up the hill, down, around, across the villa courtyard — to be escorted by the smiling Alberto right into the enormous purple bedroom.

"Good morning, sir!" Nicolò said.

"Good morning, Nicolò!"

Di Negro, in a gold dressing gown, reclined against pillows in the center of the big bed. He touched his upper lip with his forefinger, smoothing the silky moustache.

"Here —" He handed him a cup of chocolate. "Have this. And some of these."

"Biscotti?" Nicolò giggled.

The Marquis popped a fig into his mouth. "*Mangiate bene!*" he said.

"No, thank you," Nicolò replied. "I'm not hungry." It slipped out! He hadn't meant to say it — not here, when the food was real!

"Nonsense! There's more!" Di Negro waved a hand to an épergne laden with fruit. "Cherries, figs. Eat up! We'll just throw what's left into the sea." He sat up. "Who's that behind you?"

Nicolò moved to one side. "Germi," he said, with a wide grin, "may I present the Marquis Di Negro!"

"How do you do, sir?" Germi leaned over the foot of the bed. The Marquis straightened his long legs, exposing a bare ankle. Germi said, "Your foot, sir, is out of the covers."

Laughing, then, they explained their amusement, and Di Negro enjoyed every word of the recital. He flashed his teeth, smacked his lips. Finally, inhaling snuff, he dusted the front of his dressing gown with a napkin.

"This is the most fun I've had in Genoa!" he told them.

"Now — get out, both of you! There's much to do — grounds to be cleaned, new statues ordered for the garden, the grand salon opened. Friends will gather here to forget the deplorable state of the world!" He threw back the covers, overturning the chocolate pot. "And on your way out, tell that miserable Alberto to bring a mop!"

9

Restoring the villa immediately and lavishly, the Marquis launched into an endless round of soirees and fetes, offering them eagerly, as antidotes for tension and concern.

"We have to let off steam somewhere," he said. "The whole country is rattling with musketry! Peasant bands pillaging, mountain roads infested with bandits."

Someone replied, "It'll be different, soon, if persisting rumors are true. That astonishing General Buonaparte will push the Austrians out of Italy!"

"The demons won't give up," another warned, "you can bet on it — before shedding the blood of every peasant!"

"At any rate," continued Di Negro, peeling his fruit into a silver bowl of water, "when we're together here, we can look the other way for a while, escape from unpleasant thoughts."

Nicolò knew that in later years he would reflect upon his association with Di Negro as one of the richest of his life. He was delighted with the quality and extent of Di Negro's "polish," and he was gratefully aware of his own increasing luster. In the urbane society of the Marquis' friends, he acquired poise, mannerliness, a quiet confidence in himself. He memorized certain phrases until he could list them in a notebook. They would come in handy in later life, when he wished to indulge in "graceful" correspondence. Each day he added one new word to his vocabulary and set about becoming punctiliously correct. As Di Negro gave him assurance, he knew that he would never again, by telltale habit of speech or behavior, reveal his lack of education. A spindling plant nurtured to full foliage, he blossomed in Di Negro's patronage. Enjoying the run of the library, he examined the works of Corelli; Vivaldi, the Venetian red priest who supposedly halted his Mass to write the theme of a concerto; Tartini, the builder of a new "magic" wand; and more recent artists —Viotti and his teacher Pugnani. One evening he complained to Di Negro:

"Most of these works are laid out like a formal garden!"

"Is that bad?" The Marquis laughed heartily. "I'm rather proud of the geometrical elegance of the one outside this window!"

Nicolò flushed. "I didn't intend to be rude."

"You aren't. I just don't understand music." He chuckled. "I'm a natural catastrophe—an Italian who can't even carry a tune!"

"Your garden," Nicolò said, "and all the rest are beautiful — and identical. That's the problem! My garden of music must be laid out differently, so that it's the only one of its kind. . . . I can do that with fingering, harmonics." He bent over a page, only vaguely aware that Di Negro had slipped from the room.

Surprisingly enough, Antonio chose to ignore his son's new association except to grumble, "The boy'll be well out of it soon, in Parma." Taking his mandolin, he left for his favorite haunt.

His mother — he could always count on his mother! She was pleased and proud when Nicolò described the gardens, the rooms, the exciting celebrities and foreigners who moved in his new elegant world. As she listened, she altered an old suit of Carlo's.

"It's too big and too little for you, in the wrong places, Nicolò!" she admitted. "I'm afraid your arms will stick out like sticks!"

"It won't matter," he said. "I'll have on new shoes." Happiness warmed him as he remembered the shoes, wrapped in paper and put away in a box under his bed.

On the day of the musicale, the villa hummed in pleasant confusion. This would be the largest and most distinguished gathering so far, with a few guests arriving from out of town. The Marquis was everywhere at once, adding personal and audible supervision to the preparations. "Alberto!" His voice was merry. "Lots of candles! Ladies glow more beautifully in candlelight than their diamonds!" In the library, Nicolò tuned his violin, removed his coat. As his mother had predicted, his arms did protrude like sticks and the shoulders were tight, but the new shoes in which he wiggled his toes deliciously were soft as the underside of a gull.

The sound of horses pawing and snorting in the court-yard announced the guests. There was another sound! A trill of silver-bell laughter! Lisa was here — in this house — in the grand salon! Nicolò lost precious seconds getting into his coat, making his way through the assemblage. She was talking gaily with friends.

"Lisa!" he said, and she whirled about. Her face lighted up when she saw him.

"Nicolò! How delightful!" And she slipped her arm in his naturally — as though she'd been waiting for him. Her dress shimmered. It was a rich blue, the same color as the flowers in her hair. She wore a necklace of tiny pearls, and white gloves.

"Paganini!" Colonel Livron grasped his hand. "This is a pleasure. I hope it means that, at last, I am to have the privilege of enjoying your music!"

"It is my pleasure, sir, to play for you." Nicolò kept his voice low, remembering that this was a mark of good breeding.

Di Negro, affable and effusive, greeted guests on all sides, the silky moustache as carefully groomed as the rest of him. His frock coat in a romantic shade of puce with velvet collar was in harmony with his billowing cravat. Clapping for attention, he announced:

"Signor Paganini, who is honoring us today with a violin recital."

Nicolò acknowledged spontaneous exclamations as he scanned the room. They weren't all seated yet. He had a few minutes. Still smiling, he said aside to Lisa, "I have something to tell you. It can't wait."

"Why does it have to?" Her eyes danced. They sat on a sofa, half-concealed by an urn of coral flowers.

"Today," he said, "I'll play three selections. Listen, especially, to the last one."

"Why?"

"You'll find out later."

"That's not fair! Nicolò — why?"

"Later." Taking his violin, he walked to the raised stand at one end of the salon. Winning his audience with his Carmagnole variations, he began his second number, a whimsical gavotte which matched the mood of the party. He'd nearly finished when there was a loud screech. His right sleeve split at the armhole, tearing across his chest. His face caught on fire. He switched to a long glissando, ending the selection. Now the sleeve wrinkled and sagged down his arm. A loud guffaw rose and died suddenly as Di Negro stood up.

"A thousand pardons, Signor Paganini," he said. "But I find this room much too warm!" He summoned Alberto to open the windows at once. Smoothing his silky moustache, he continued, "And now, if the ladies will forgive us." He removed his coat, folded it over the back of his chair and waited, at ease, until every man in the room had done likewise. Nicolò laid his bow across the music stand and peeled off his own wretched garment. The Marquis re-seated himself, winked imperceptibly, and leaned back in his chair.

The opening bars of the Silver Étude sprang from

Nicolò's lightning fingers, every note pure and perfect. Lisa sat forward. She cocked her head to one side, rewarding him with a dazzling smile. Servants crowded the door. Before the final note died away, the distinguished listeners were all around him, exclaiming, praising.

"Nicolò!" Lisa found his hand. Her dimple appeared, her dark eyes flashed. "Now tell me, what was it?"

"I call it the Silver Étude." He was enjoying her impatience.

"Perfect!" She added, "All the time I was listening, I had the feeling it was somehow very special." He clasped her fingers tighter.

"It was — it is — it's full title is 'Lisa's Silver Étude.' I wrote it for you." A sudden pinkness suffused her face.

"Thank you, Nicolò." She smiled, shyly. "I am honored." She stood on tiptoe to whisper, "Whatever else you write, it will always be my own favorite."

"I'm glad you —" All at once he was flustered, tongue-tied. He released her hand quickly, giddy with relief as Livron and Di Negro materialized at his elbow.

"There are some Italians," the Colonel was saying, "who long to taste the fruit of liberty. It's high time Italy was counted among free nations!" Politics. Everywhere, the talk was politics and war, war and politics. Not so today, however. Today it was poetry. Nicolò listened attentively. At the door, as the Livrons were leaving, he said, "When are you coming back to Genoa?"

Lisa said gaily, "Turn about, you know. Come to visit us, next time, in Leghorn!"

"When?"

"Whenever you can!" Impulsively, she took a flower from her hair, pressed it into his hand. "If it isn't soon, I'll send you another like it, to remind you!" Livron shook his hand.

"Don't disappoint us, Paganini. We'll expect you."

When all the guests had departed, Nicolò said, "Today, this afternoon. I deeply appreciate —"

"Nonsense! It gave me the excuse I was after." The Marquis seated himself behind the desk. "Your third number? Charming! Reminiscent, in places, of Mozart's airy grace."

"Mozart!" Nicolò fairly shrieked. "Then I'll shred it into confetti for a street carnival!"

"Go ahead! What's one composition more or less? You can always write another."

"Hold on!" Nicolò snapped. "It isn't that easy. Besides, what do you know about it?" This was one subject they'd never discussed, and he preferred to leave it at that. "You couldn't possibly understand." He planted both feet widely apart, expecting retaliation, and was taken aback at Di Negro's utter lack of hostility. The Marquis' face was serene. "I'm sorry," he said contritely, "there's no need to take it out on you. I'll just destroy it, that's all."

Di Negro laughed. "Exactly. That's what I did."

"W—what?" Nicolò sat on the edge of a chair. "What — when?"

"In Rome. When a friend compared my work to another poet's. I flew into a temper and burned my manuscript. Watched until it was ashes. I got even with that poet! I showed him a thing or two!" At the thought of the jovial Marquis in a temper, Nicolò had to smile.

"Did it help?" he asked.

"Certainly!" A line formed between his brows. "But I've never figured out just who. My friend said, 'What did you do that for?' The poet never heard of me, probably hasn't, to this day — and I lost the most beautiful, most sensitive piece of work I'd ever written. I've been sorry ever since."

"Then how can you laugh?"

"To remind myself what a fool I was. When I tried to answer my friend, I discovered why I had burned the manuscript. It wasn't to get even." Little flutterings in Nicolò's stomach said, "Don't trespass here." This was clearly something he didn't want to think about. Di Negro shrugged. "I've ordered roses for the garden. Which of the other flowers should I weed out?"

"Why — none! You've plenty of ground. Just add the roses. The more color, variety — the prettier!" Di Negro made no reply. Nicolò's mouth flew open. "You're the clever one! You have just said that I'm different from Mozart and he's different from me — but we both have a place in the garden!"

"*You* said it!" Di Negro smiled.

That was odd! Already, his insides were settling down. Mozart was something more than a menace! He was a person, an artist — who had pored over his work late into the night, writing, changing, adding, perspiring, becoming discouraged. . . .

Nicolò said, "He probably worked as hard as I do!"

"No doubt. The real meaning of art is that it doesn't have to be, it shouldn't be alike. Each artist expresses what is uniquely his own. He does not take his talent from another artist — nor make it less than it is."

"All those stories of his exciting childhood, and yet Mozart must have been even worse off than I am if he had to be buried in a pauper's cemetery. Why did that happen?"

"Greatness is rarely recognized in its own time. He was buried in an unmarked grave but he raised his own monument in the memories and hearts of men." Nicolò grew very still. He said:

"My father doesn't understand any of this. If he did, he'd let me alone!" The Marquis turned up his palms.

"The artichoke, again!" he exclaimed. "Getting to the heart of a man is like peeling it! The outside keeps coming off in layers until the core is reached. You'll get it all figured out one day," he assured the boy.

On the way out, Nicolò hesitated. "I never really hated Mozart," he told the Marquis. "I just found out why I thought I did. You won't tell anyone if I tell you?"

"Never"

"I was afraid of him — and jealous. I don't think I am now. Not any more." He smiled secretly. "Why did you burn your manuscript?" He didn't expect an answer. He already had it.

Di Negro nodded, murmuring, "Mmmm. . . ."

It was late when he left the villa. The Carrughi, labyrinth of alleyways twisting snakelike through the Passo, was deserted and dark. Nicolò knew every inch and was unafraid, even though the district was considered unsafe. Violin in hand, he hurried along, recalling the nasal tone of Di Negro's voice, eager to try an experiment. If he tuned the rest of the strings a little off key, keeping the G in pitch, it was possible. . . .

A figure moved, up ahead. Was there something familiar about the man's walk, the hunch of his shoulders. . . .? By-passing the state buildings, he turned the corner. Certain, now, of the man's identity, Nicolò followed, keeping to the shadows. What was the Colonel doing here, at this time of night? Livron went up an outside flight of steps to a second story, along an overhanging corridor-balcony, halting at a closed door. Before he could knock, it opened wide from the inside. A hearty voice said:

"Colonel! Come in! Your punctuality is admirable, but from you I expected nothing less." Nicolò was grateful for the light streaming from the room for he saw the speaker distinctly. About twenty-six, with a small, almost dwarfish figure, he was unusually thin, with lank hair drooping to his shoulders. But for all of that, he displayed a vigorous energy. As they went inside, closing the door behind them, Nicolò came closer, carefully laid his case at his feet, and looked through the window. He saw Livron stop beside a large table littered with maps, quills, drawings.

The small man said, "Other lists show a knowledge of passes, snows, weather."

As they seated themselves, Livron told the other man: "Allow me to say that I am overwhelmed by the cascade of plans that pours from you. I remember so well, in Paris. . . . Your ideas are brilliant and bold. We must examine them closely." He bent over the table.

"I came because —" Despite his shabbiness, the small

man had a dignity that was almost regal. Nicolò noticed that his bright eyes lacked warmth. The stranger was saying, "Genoa is full of diplomats, agents. Here, one with sharp eyes, keen ears, and a silent mouth can learn a great deal."

Livron nodded. "The ideas of the Revolution," he said, "crossed the frontiers years ago. Italy is laced with revolt, leaders clamoring for 'Italia Unita.'" As the Colonel turned his head aside, his voice blurred. Nicolò strained to hear. "Your reputation as the rising new star in the firmament doesn't surprise me. What better person than a man of Italian blood, bearing an Italian name and speaking Italian to be the herald of liberty and equality."

"Just what do you think you're doing here?" The low, crackly voice at Nicolò's elbow took the breath out of his body. His head snapped.

"I — er —" He picked up his violin, tried to recover his speech. The old crone snatched at his arm with fingers like talons.

"Nosy, aren't you, sonny?" She kept her voice in her throat. "Peering in at windows into matters that are no concern of yours can get you in a heap of bad trouble!" Her hair was an abandoned bird's nest, twiglike wisps trailing over her ears.

Nicolò whispered, "I'm going — was just on my way. You see, the Colonel, in there, is a friend of mine." He jerked his head.

"Colonel, did you say?" She snickered contemptuously. "You can bet your life he isn't! He's a general, that's what he is! And I promised him privacy. Now, you get along! If General Buonaparte —"

"Napoleon Buonaparte?" Nicolò almost choked. "I don't believe it! He'd be older. And he'd look different, too!" He didn't know, exactly, what he expected, but certainly not this scrawny person with scurf upon his collar and ill-fitting boots!

"He's old enough," she said. "And after he says a few words to you, his looks don't matter. Now, get on with you or I'll call the General."

Without a backward glance Nicolò scurried down the steps, not altering his running pace for several alleys. At a safe distance, he slowed to catch his breath then resumed a normal gait. So this was the man who was being talked about everywhere! The man whose name was hailed by the masses. This was the man who would make his way by the sword? "Well, go to it, General," Nicolò said aloud. "But my way is better. I'll make my way by the violin!"

10

At breakfast, Antonio, in bad temper, complained without let-up. Finally he pushed his plate away.

"My ticket didn't win," he said. "You can forget Parma."

"Forget?" Nicolò sprang from his chair. "But it's all right now! Germi, too, is going to Parma — he will study at the University."

"I'll enter you in the Conservatory, here," Antonio concluded, disregarding his son's outburst. Nicolò's stomach knotted, thinking of the rigid classes, exercises, routines. . . .

"No, Father!" he said.

"Don't defy me!" Antonio shook his fist.

"I'll smother at the Conservatory," Nicolò pleaded. "Don't you see?"

"I see — that you're always on the opposite side!"

It was true. The distance between father and son was a

million miles wide. Nicolò wished he could cross the distance as easily as he now stepped to his father's side. He wanted to shout, You are always against me! Nothing I have ever done pleases you! But he was determined to keep his thoughts to himself. ·

"I don't always want to be at odds with you, Father."

"Then stop your arguments," Antonio shouted. He trailed off with less conviction: ". . . Balking me at every turn! I'll check into the Conservatory." Nicolò clenched his hands behind his back.

"About Parma," he said, "we must think of something!"

"*We?*" A new light shone in his father's eyes. He reached out as if to touch Nicolò's shoulder then dropped his arm. He said, awkwardly, "Good-bye." Letting himself out, he immediately stuck his head back in the doorway. "See that you're practicing tonight when I get home!" The words were the same but they had lost their sting, and the light was still there, making Antonio's eyes glisten.

Nicolò put a fresh string in his fiddle, spat on his shoes, shining them with a rag, and left for the villa. He walked slowly, weighed down by his disappointment.

When they met, Germi took one look at his friend and said: "Your mouth's wearing those *f* holes on each side. What's wrong?"

"The Madonna answered my prayer." Nicolò sighed. "I forgot to cancel it. Now I'm not going to Parma!"

Later, in Di Negro's library, the Marquis listened and nodded sympathetically as he stroked his silky moustache. "Germi and I have changed places, that's all!" Nicolò said. "Everything's as bad as before, only in reverse!"

"Reason indicates," Germi said as his eyes crinkled, "that what we have to do now is think our way out of it."

"Reason!" Nicolò grumbled.

Di Negro ticked off his fingers. "One, you need money. Two, you don't have it. Three, how to get it? Four, you can't steal it and the chances of finding it are pretty slim; so —"

Germi said, matter-of-factly, "You earn it."

Nicolò jumped off the floor. "The debut concert, of course!" he shrieked. "Why didn't I think of it?"

"Because you have me," Germi laughed. "Use your brains for what God intended!"

Di Negro opened a drawer. "Here's paper," he said.

"Paper?"

"Of course, paper! To outline plans." Di Negro chuckled as he picked up a quill. "I'll inform every person I know that to continue in my good graces, he must purchase a seat to the forthcoming Paganini debut."

The next few weeks were chaotic. Elated by the prospect of collecting money, Antonio assumed the task of choosing the hall. The Marquis consulted newspaper offices on prices of advertising and concentrated on his list which lengthened each day. Germi drafted notice after notice until he was satisfied with what he'd written. When Nicolò cancelled his wharf concerts, in order to devote more time to lessons and rehearsals, his friends fanned out through the city to spread the news of the coming debut. His mother patched the tear in his jacket and reset the sleeves to avoid what had happened at Di Negro's. At Nicolò's dictation, Germi wrote to Lisa and the Colonel. Nicolò thought of inviting

116

Buonaparte but he didn't know where to find the General. He inquired in the Passo only to find an empty room. He heard many stories about Buonaparte's activities — but he was only puzzled by the different reports. Some saw the little General as a savior — others feared and loathed him. Nicolò said it proved that politics could not be understood.

One evening, at home, Antonio informed them, "I've rented the Teatro Sant 'Agostino. In order to do it, I had to guarantee the orchestra fees, agree to bear all financial risks. . . ."

"Why?" Germi frowned.

Nicolò jumped at the opportunity to comment on a subject with which he was totally familiar. He said, "If I were engaged by the impresario to perform the 'intermezzo concert,' between the numbers of a scheduled double bill, then I would receive a percentage of receipts. Otherwise —" he shrugged — "our share is what's left *after* all expenses."

"After expenses!" Germi said. "Do you think there'll be anything left for Parma?"

"Certainly. More than enough!" Nicolò was indignant. "This is my *paese,* my country. I'm not unknown. My last performance at the theater wasn't exactly a flop!"

Antonio's eyes gleamed. "That's it!" he said. "Germi, re-word the notice to read that the great Marchesi is guest performer! We'll have a sell-out!"

"No!" Nicolò's nostrils flared. "This is a Paganini debut. I won't have people buying seats because of Marchesi!"

"Why not?" Antonio wanted to know. "If he can make us richer, why not?"

"First of all," Nicolò said, "ours is a gentleman's agree-

117

ment. His is a courtesy appearance." His lip trembled. "All my life you've pushed me to the day when I would be paid for my work! Throwing Mozart in my face —" Nicolò's mouth twisted out of shape. "And now that the moment is here," he cried, "you dare to suggest that I march under false colors! You want Marchesi to guarantee receipts! Why? I'll tell you. Because you think that I, alone, cannot do it! Where is your faith in me?"

His father's face was the color of wet stucco.

"Be quiet!" he shouted. "It's no crime to announce . . . Marchesi fills the theater! He's a big name. You are beginning. Why take a chance?"

"What do you mean, why take a chance? You take chances every day of your life — on a winning ticket!" Antonio half-rose from his chair. A dark red blood vessel bulged in his temple. His hands shook. It was a nasty thing to say. Why doesn't he beat me? Nicolò wondered. It wouldn't pain as badly as this sickening ache. In all the suffering at his father's hand, he'd never been wounded so much on the inside and it was like having his chest crushed. "Besides," he said woodenly, "it isn't the same thing. I must do this on my own. By myself."

"Alone?" Antonio sounded out of breath, frightened.

Frightened? That was it! Yes, that had to be it! His father was afraid, afraid for him, afraid that he might fail! Accustomed to nothing but taunts and belittling remarks for his free concerts, Nicolò was struck by his turnabout! In spite of himself he laughed out loud. Germi snickered, then giggled, unable to stop. Antonio looked from one to the other. His mouth upturned slightly at the corners.

118

Color came back in his face. Nicolò laughed louder. Germi's giggles ranged higher. Antonio snorted, threw back his head and guffawed from his stomach. Their voices rocked the room. Finally, wiping their eyes, they sat, exhausted, in the first happy silence that Nicolò could remember.

On July twenty-fifth, as Nicolò and Germi entered the library, Di Negro's running footsteps sounded in the corridor.

"Here it is!" He followed his voice into the room, excitedly waving the Genoa *Avvisi*. "See?" He pointed, "Right there!" and shoved the paper under their noses. Nicolò stared. In black letters, his own name sprang at him, starting somersaults in his stomach.

"Read it," he said to Di Negro. "Please read it slowly." The Marquis smoothed his moustache and read in a booming voice:

"There will be a concert in the Teatro Sant 'Agostino next Friday, July 31. It will be given by Nicolò Paganini, of Genoa, a boy already known in his *paese* for his skill as a violinist. Having decided to go to Parma to perfect himself in his profession under the guidance of the renowned Professor Rolla, and not being in a position to defray the many necessary expenses, he has conceived this plan to give him courage to ask his fellow citizens to contribute towards his project, thereby inviting them to be present at this event which he hopes will prove enenjoyable."*

*From *Paganini, the Genoese*, Vol. I, by G. I. C. de Courcy, University of Oklahoma Press, 1957.

He clapped Germi's shoulder. "That's about the finest writing I've seen!" Germi's smile went to his ears.

Di Negro cleared his throat. "Uh, Nicolò. There is other news. Disappointing, I'm afraid." Nicolò heard with only half his mind. Tingling with excitement he thought, This is it — the first step! He'd been beaten, locked in his room, further imprisoned by his own self-discipline, yet he'd go through it all again. Yes, it was worth it!

"Er, what did you say?"

"A message from Leghorn. The Colonel conveys his and Lisa's best wishes and regrets. She, unfortunately, is indisposed." The sun went behind a cloud, dimming the room. A draft of air blew cool on his neck.

"It's all right," he said. "There will be more concerts. Besides, she'll be listening." Sunlight glowed again, as the cloud passed and a delicate scent of lilacs floated in the room.

"Marchesi?" Germi asked.

"No word from him yet." Di Negro speculated, "Probably, on the next boat. If he sent a letter by stage, it may never arrive. What with wretched cutthroats, ambushed revolutionaries, bandit-ridden highways, Italy sits on a volcano every bit as menacing as old walrus-hide Vesuvius fomenting to eruption!"

"He'll be here," Nicolò said. "Whether he writes or not. Because he said he would."

Marchesi's message came just ahead of the singer himself. Brief, written in brown ink on jonquil-colored paper, in curly flowing letters, it said, "To the sublime Paganini, greetings! All activities are dwarfed by the anticipated experience of Friday next. I'll be there!"

120

And he was. Backstage, Nicolò, assailed by the sudden scent of lavender, said, "Marchesi!"

"You smelled him, too?" Germi said. "Come on!" They ran through the wings.

"Where is he?" Marchesi's delightful treble came from the stage door. "Pa-g-a-nnn-i-n-i?" They dived around an urn, slipped up behind him. In a loud voice, Nicolò said:

"Do you mean *Nicolò* Paganini?" Marchesi whirled, his teeth flashing like polished grains of young corn.

"Divine boy-genius!" he squealed, "and the wizard manager!" His shoes were a startling vermilion with glistening buckles. Taking a small vial from his pocket, he lifted it to his lips, then gargled merrily, spitting into the urn.

"That's part of the scenery!" a passing stagehand cried. Marchesi made a face at the man's back and opened his mouth. A perfect high C reverberated to the dome. The stagehand spun around. Descending the scale, Marchesi broke into an aria. Spontaneously, the man joined in, and Nicolò and Germi added their voices. When they tailed off, laughing, the man scurried away, saying, "*Grazie, grazie.* Wait until I tell the *bambini* that I sang with Marchesi!"

Antonio ran up to report, "If you need me for anything, I'll be at the box office. Receipts are pouring in. House is stuffed!"

Marchesi, in his suit of armor, gave his usual spectacular performance. Listening in the wings, Nicolò viewed the house, recalling an earlier remark of Germi's: "Di Negro's box is filled, tonight, mostly with beautiful ladies."

Taking his violin, Nicolò stepped to the footlights,

121

acknowledging the applause from ladies as beautiful and colorful as flowers. Tonight, however, they were only the setting for a very special blossom. His glance swept the pit until he found her. His mother sat between the girls, her hands at ease in her lap. She had brightened her black dress with a touch of white at the throat. He met her glance and smiled. Then Nicolò nodded to the conductor, arched his wrist and let his bow fall upon the strings. . . .

He played effortlessly, and before his first number had ended he knew he had captured his audience. There were shouts of "Bravo!" and tears. When they were silent, they sat with amazed faces. At the end of the concert, Di Negro and his friends, followed by the entire house, rose to give the young virtuoso a standing ovation. And then they wouldn't let him stop! He had played three encores when there was a commotion at the back of the theater. Nicolò motioned for silence. He stepped to the footlights and leaned forward.

"Germi," he called. "What's the matter?"

"You're what's the matter, Nicolò," Germi answered softly. "A crowd has gathered on the street. They say it's the music of heaven! They couldn't buy tickets. They just wanted to listen. I'll get rid of them."

"Let them in, Germi."

"What?"

"Let them stand in the back. I want to play one selection — just for them."

"Yes, Maestro!" Germi grinned.

Finally, when it was really over, Nicolò Paganini was carried from the stage, down into the pit where the laughing, shouting crowd swarmed over him. And then they were separating on either side, making an aisle from him to his father, who came in a hurry along the lane as the cheering crowd closed in behind him. On a plaited ribbon chain around his neck he wore a big, round, shiny medallion that bounced as he walked. At Nicolò's side he said:

"And now I present the colors of the house of Paganini to celebrate this occasion!" He lifted the chain, placing it around Nicolò's neck. More cheers went up.

Nicolò fingered the disk and howled in pleasure. "Father, it's a packing seal!"

"It was. Now it's a Paganini shield! I chose the colors for a reason." He announced in a loud voice, "The orange is for genius — my son's genius that burns like a fire. . . ." He waited for the shouts to die down. "And the blue is for the color of the sea and sky — the color of Genoa, the land of his birth, and," he finished hoarsely, "the white is for faith — belief — which we must all have in him if he is to succeed!" He winked at Nicolò.

"Thank you, Father." It was all he could manage at the moment. Then he laughed and whispered, "I feel like a prize barrel of pickles!"

Antonio slapped him on the shoulder. He said, "It isn't every day you want to hang a medal on somebody. That's only when you wake up and find out they're special!"

There was one other passenger in the stagecoach. Nondescript, he kept to himself, grumbling continuously. "This is a road? Ha! Such jostling, tossing, so that a man's hard put to keep his teeth in his head!" At the next posting station where they changed horses, he left them, relieved to be "still of a piece!" Bouncing easily on the seat, Nicolò told Germi:

"You see, it's what goes on in a man's head that really counts. The man who just left was angry because he had to make the trip. Now, my father —" he looked to the back of the coach where Antonio snored, his mouth slack — "with money in his pocket is sleeping as peacefully as he does in his own bed. And you and I? We're too happy to complain, too excited to sleep!"

The sun was dropping to the horizon. Pretty soon it would be time for the driver to stop the stage and light the lanterns. Nicolò watched as shadows changed the landscape. Emerald grass went gray in the waning light. Ahead, in the foothills, tall trees waved arms of weedlike branches. They clopped through a bright unobstructed clearing and Nicolò decided the world was light and dark — a continuous contrast of color! Shadows, then, in music — shading — must be as important as the sunshine melody!

Suddenly, violent shouts erupted from the roadside. The coach lurched, buckled, nearly overturning as the driver reined in the frightened horses. Loud neighs rose in the confusion of strident voices. Inside, they were thrown like rag dolls to the floor. Germi yelled, Antonio groaned. A hot pain in his own head cut off Nicolò's hearing.

He couldn't have been out long, for, as he regained his senses, he heard Germi being ordered from the coach.

"Over here," a guttural voice in the bushes commanded. Nicolò lay still on the floor. His father! What had they

124

done with his father? He found the lump on his head. It throbbed like a stone bruise.

Near at hand a voice said, "Pago! There's another one inside. Knocked out!"

"Leave him alone. He'll be easy. No struggling." The guttural voice belonged to Pago, the leader. Nicolò shot up, straining to see. A chill took hold of him. The bandits, at least a dozen, all brandishing knives, were enjoying themselves. Tying the driver to a tree, one bandit jerked off his shoes while another tore at his jacket. "My size!" he exclaimed.

Pago struck the speaker. "Pile his clothes, there," he said. "I'll say who gets what!"

"This one wants to fight!" Nicolò saw his father then, struggling with a man twice his size. No mean adversary, nevertheless he was kicked and pounded as though he were a midget. Once he broke away, puffing with rage, but powerful arms pulled him back. A blade flashed against his throat.

"No!" Nicolò's shriek brought Pago to the coach.

"Out!" he said. "With the rest." His breath was foul. A wide, bumpy scar gulleyed his cheek, curved into his mouth. A big, round ring dangled from his ear. Nicolò recalled stories about a certain tribe with this talisman who never killed its victims outright, but tortured them, left them to die slowly. "Move!" Pago knocked him to the ground, flicked his chin with a blade. Nicolò touched the stinging spot, wiped away a warm trickle. A bandit with one eye stood guard over Germi. Unable to read the message in his

125

friend's eyes, Nicolò answered silently, Whatever you do, *amico,* just hurry. We haven't much time.

"Let's get it over with," the big man said. Surly at the discovery that they'd waylaid travelers destitute as themselves, the ruffians were tiring of their game. "They're not worth the trouble. No jewelry — no fine clothes —"

"The old man first." Pago told Antonio, "Empty your pockets. You won't need money where you're going."

Money? Nicolò gasped. The concert receipts? Even if they survived, there'd be no Parma, no Professor Rolla.

"Pago." Germi's voice was high-pitched, quavering. Nicolò prayed: *Blessed Mother, please send him an extra dose of reason.* "I must warn you. " Apparently Germi had thought of something!

"Warn *me?*" Pago howled. "Of what?"

Germi pointed to Nicolò.

"This one, here, is a black witch! If you let us go, now, you're safe. Otherwise —" Germi rolled his eyes, held his stomach. "Awful things will happen!" The superstitious bandits drew near but kept behind Pago. Only the big man remained with Antonio, but he had put away his knife. The driver whimpered.

"Ho, ho!" Pago's lips spread crookedly. "You don't say! Comes closer to looking like a scared buzzard!" He glanced expectantly at the others. Their laughter was thin, sickly. The big man pushed Antonio forward.

"Let him work his black deviltry," he said. "I know where there's a white witch. A white witch can undo black magic!" Exclamations of relief rumbled all around. Pago's blade whipped past Germi's ear.

126

"Thought you had us, didn't you?" The whole forest began to swim around Nicolò. His teeth chattered. He shut his eyes.

"Come closer," Germi said. They moved in, Antonio, also, his eyes alert. He's as dumfounded as they are, Nicolò thought. As I am. Germi whispered, "He, the one on the ground, is *both!* A black and a white witch! These doubles, only a few in all of Italy, are born every fourth generation when Scorpio is in opposition to Pisces." How did Germi think up such twaddle? But with his eerie tone, anyone would believe him. Germi could convince a fish he couldn't swim. As though he pronounced sentence, Germi concluded, "Nothing can break his spell!"

"Don't believe him!" the big man shouted.

"Come to think of it," one of the ruffians muttered, "he does look unlike the other two — with that beak nose." Nicolò smiled into the grass. Now he knew he hadn't been born ugly for nothing!

Pago said, "You're lying!" His eyes shifted from side to side, seeking something to satisfy his gang. All at once he laughed. "Then prove it!" he said. "If it's true, then prove it!" The big man stepped back. "But not on me!" he added, completely destroying his speech about the white witch. "No hexes on me! I don't aim to have a fire in my belly for the rest of my life, or watch my hand grow into a claw!"

"Me neither!" Loud protests followed. "Pago, let's get out!"

"Shut up, all of you. I said he'll prove it and what I say is law!"

"Then let him prove it on you!" somebody snarled. Pago started to strike the speaker when sudden fear filled his

127

face. A real scoundrel, he was brave only when the danger threatened someone else.

Germi played his advantage, saying, "The proof is terrible to see." Antonio nodded vigorously. Thank goodness, the gang had no way of knowing he was indicating moral support of Germi rather than verification of what he said. "However," Germi acted as though he shared a valuable secret, "he can prove it another way — that's completely harmless."

Nicolò groaned aloud. What could he prove, lying on the grass, hardly daring to breathe? Suppose he stood, what could he do — make faces? If only they'd listened to Di Negro. He'd warned, "Take the long way — by boat."

Pago moistened his lips, fighting a losing battle. He was known for his cruelty and fearlessness; he couldn't afford to be duped. But being hexed was even worse! Either way, he'd lose his role as leader. Pago didn't answer and that was answer enough.

"Fetch your violin, Nicolò," Germi said. "From the coach."

"The witch is also a fiddler!" a bandit shrieked. Past thinking, Nicolò followed Germi's direction automatically. Their lives hung on the next minutes, and he prayed again that Germi's supply of reason was holding out. His grandfather's words whispered in his ear. "Keep it with you. It will always bring good luck." Furiously, Nicolò's hand sought the case. His chest contracted. The snuffbox wasn't there! Had he forgotten it? Lost it? Left it at home?

"Watch him!" someone shouted. "He may have pistols in that sack!" Pago wrenched the violin from Nicolò's hand, peeled down the case and threw it on the ground. He sneered:

"It is only a fiddle!" Recovering the Amati and bow, Nicolò stood beside Germi, who told them:

"The witch has imprisoned your souls in here." He touched the belly of the violin. "In order to free them, you must run. Don't look back, even once!"

With a great show of bravado, Pago said, "You can't scare us with this thin waif and a battered old fiddle!"

"Listen!" Germi said. "Listen, and your souls will speak to you in many voices!" He nudged Nicolo. *"Play!"* he ordered.

Nicolò tucked the violin under his chin, raised the bow and froze, with fingers glued to the stick. Antonio coughed, the bandits growled. Pago swept the case from the ground, shook it.

"We're waiting to hear the voices of our souls, ha, ha!" He waved the case over his head when plop, the little snuffbox hit the earth! Germi dived for it.

"His special rosin," he said. "Made from devil's snuff." He handed the box to Nicolò who suddenly felt warm. A glow, spreading down his arms, loosened his fingers. It also enabled him to plant his feet firmly, to raise his head, to set his eyes staring boldly. . . .

The scream that issued from the fingerboard sent the bandits back on their heels. Some fell to their knees. Nicolò's violin was a screeching demon, a heavenly harp with a tone so exquisite that it backed Pago against a stump.

"It's an angel singing!" he gasped.

A night bird rustled nearby, its keening cry lacing the

stillness. Instantly, Nicolò repeated the bird call and the bird flew low, straining its throat in song. Nicolò played on and on. From the squawking of chickens and bleating goats to a sobbing sweet cry, no note was unintentional. His hand obeyed a mysterious control, led by inner inspiration.

One ruffian turned and ran. Another followed. Without a backward glance, Pago plunged into the night, with the rest of the gang right behind him. Only the echo of running feet came from the hills.

Antonio unbound the driver. "Here are your clothes," he said. "Hurry. I'll light the lanterns." In minutes they were on their way. Antonio ran a hand over his face. "Good lad, Germi, whatever made you think of that?"

"Now, whatever else was there to do?" Nicolò told his father. Germi gave him a big fat wink as the coach galloped toward Parma.

11

Through hoary chestnut groves spotted with the ruins of Roman villas built as early as 183 B.C., they entered the ancient city of Parma. Everywhere huge red-purple violets perfumed the air and the octagonal baptistry with its five colonnaded galleries placed one above the other stood tall in Piazza Duomo. Alighting from the coach, they separated, Germi heading toward the old University.

"*Arrivederci*," he said. "Nicolò, you know where to find me." He shook Antonio's hand. "Good-bye, sir." Obtaining directions to Rolla's house, Nicolò and his father set out on foot.

At the door, the maestro's wife informed them, "The signor is ill. He will see no one!"

"But I have papers!" Antonio indicated his valise. "Credentials!"

Her face softened. "Another time?" she said.

"We have come all the way from Genoa!" Nicolò said sadly.

"I *am* sorry!" She began to close the door.

"At home," Nicolò blurted, "I gave a concert to raise money. So we could get here. We almost didn't — bandits in the hills." He brushed a curl from his eye. "If you asked him —?"

"I'm afraid it's useless." She opened the door wider. "But step inside. Tell me your name."

Seating them in a large, airy room crowded with big chairs, heavy tables, she passed through a curtained doorway in the far side of the wall. His father rose again, almost at once, began to pace. Stopping at a desk in the corner, he gazed absently at the papers cluttering its surface. His body stiffened. He leaned closer. Then he motioned frantically. At that moment Rolla's voice was heard from the bedroom.

"I am dying! My whole inside is afire — belly, spine, guts! And you bother me with this — what's his name — this Paganini! Who is he? What's he doing here — in the next room!" There was a soft "*Shh.*"

At Nicolò's elbow, Antonio whispered: "Look! The ink is hardly dry!" It was the solo of a new concerto. He said, "Your violin, Nicolò!"

The professor refused to be quiet. His voice became even louder. "Importunate strangers! Get them out!"

Nicolò drew his bow and the violin sang. Ah! this was easy. The melody was autumn itself, tantalizing, mellow. It was the shadows in the glade last night, the eager

133

patches of sunlight. It was the cold avalanche of a mountain waterfall.

"Saint Theresa! Holy Mother, preserve us!" Rolla stood in the doorway, nightshirt flapping his bare feet. "I don't believe it!" He came on into the room, squinting at Nicolò. His father introduced himself and his son and Rolla raved on. "Never heard anything to compare — spontaneous, fresh — exactly what I heard in my head as I wrote it!" His wife came in with his slippers.

"You'll catch cold."

Rolla threw up his hands. "You can speak of such things at a time like this? My love, you are in the company of genius!" He kissed her soundly, allowing himself to be helped into a robe. Putting on his slippers, he sat beside Antonio, who produced letters of introduction.

"I would be honored, sir, to study with you," Nicolò said.

"Study with me?" Rolla echoed. "Ha! A crow teach a nightingale to sing? Now — Professor Paer? Yes! By all means, you must go to Paer!" He smoothed the robe across his knees. "If you please," he said. "The *soli*, again?" As Nicolò obliged, the front door was pushed slowly inward. A head with a great shock of stiff white hair peered hesitantly around the edge. At the last note, the man said:

"I was passing." His brown eyes sparkled. "I had to see who —" He spied Rolla. "Forgive me," he begged, "but I've never heard you play in such a manner!"

"Maestro!" Rolla was across the room in a leap. "Come in!" He said to the others, "Allow me to present my be-

134

loved teacher, the distinguished Neopolitan conductor, Maître Gasparo Ghiretti!" The old man was intensely pleased. He blustered:

"You were never so enthusiastic during your knuckle-rapping days!"

Rolla introduced father and son, then, as his wife brought coffee, creamy tan and hot. Ghiretti's eyes weren't brown. They were blue, almost purple, with the same velvety softness as the flowers of his adopted country.

Rolla was saying, "So I told them to seek Paer."

"Paer doesn't have time for another pupil!" Ghiretti cried. "He's stopped teaching for a while to have time to write an opera for Duke Ferdinando." Nicolò put down his cup. Rolla had refused him. . . . Paer was too busy. . . . He balled his hands to keep from sweeping the table clean. His father looked defeated.

Ghiretti smiled. The deep lines accentuating his aging face pointed up a dimple in his chin. It gave him a mischievous, elfin expression. "I wonder —" Afraid to hope, Nicolò blanked his mind. "Would you consider studying with me?"

Nicolò nearly choked. He jumped out of his chair. Rolla beamed.

"We have money," Antonio said. "It's all yours—Nicolò is not dependent on another's generosity."

Ghiretti brushed this aside, saying to Nicolò: "You're a virtuoso, lad, in technique, but that's only a part of style." His blue eyes shone. "Intuition, warmth, color, emotion — the thousand and one factors must unite. I'd like to teach

135

you what is right and wrong aesthetically — the art of clarifying." Nicolò wasn't sure he understood, unless it was more "polish." He nodded vigorously.

Outside, however, as Ghiretti walked between them, there was no trouble understanding his father. Antonio said, "Cure him of his boyish whimsies, experiments, inventions. Make him a musician!"

"He'll do that himself!" Ghiretti assured him. "His talent, like every man's, is God-given. But it must be nurtured, developed. The final achievement will come about because of his work. I hope to encourage Nicolò to express himself. The rest is up to him."

"There, Nicolò, you hear? Exactly what I've been telling you!" Antonio cried. Nicolo smiled on the inside where it wouldn't show as his father continued speaking to Ghiretti:

"I've always known he was the son on whom the pride and hopes of the family centered. Not a day has passed that I've not prodded him with every weapon I could think of. As long as I live," he finished proudly, "he can turn to me. I never succeeded, but I'll do anything to see that he does." It was strange how some people, especially fathers, kept the best part of them locked in a shell, like a coconut. If you didn't get through the solid covering, you'd never know the inside was good.

Later, after his father had returned to Genoa and he'd moved into his quarters at Ghiretti's, settling easily into his new routine, Nicolò was told one morning. "Now put away your violin."

"What do you mean?" Nicolò did not understand.

"Just what I said." Ghiretti's hair pointed in different

136

directions as if he'd forgotten to comb it. He produced quill and paper. "I think," he said, "we'll devote many lessons to counterpoint, the art of plural melody."

"That's simple." Nicolò reached for his instrument. "I can play a melody, make it move at the same time with a couple of separate melodies!"

Ghiretti shook his head. "*Without* touching the violin! Here—" Ghiretti pulled out a chair. "Sit at the desk and write what you would play."

Nicolò ruled the staffs down the page, setting the key signatures. Fingering several sheets of paper, he remarked, "I'll use these up in no time!"

"You'll not get off that easily," Ghiretti said, smiling. "There's a full quire, twenty-four sheets in the drawer." He pursed his lips. "Any more excuses?" Nicolò didn't answer. Already he was lettering black notes with flying tails across the page. Reaching the bottom, he sanded the paper, took another, and wrote at the top, "Paganini, page 2."

He saw Germi frequently but never for very long. What free time Germi had, caught up as he was in a rigid curriculum, he devoted to study. Nicolò was sympathetic.

"It takes brains to be an advocate," he told his friend. "Whereas, music — it's inside already, it just has to get out."

Germi marked the place in his book with a finger. "Book learning is book learning, something you can see and hold on to." His eyes crinkled. "I'm glad music chose you. I wouldn't know how to let it out!"

Imperceptibly, the days were shortening. Then autumn shed her golden skirts for winter's bleak-colored coat.

Christmas came and went. Nicolò rarely left his desk. His skin pulled tight over his face seemed transparent, emphasizing the sunken dark eyes, the sensitive beaklike nose. His hair grew longer, hung loosely now, the curls finally giving way. Among exercises, he wrote twenty-four fugues for four hands, duettos. Often he and Ghiretti argued over the techniques with which he experimented. Commenting on his method of tuning the strings off key, left hand *pizzicato*, double stops, Ghiretti said:

"Trying to abolish the classics?"

"Not abolish!" Nicolò insisted. "Just going around them! I can't shut off my mind. Hearing the strangest music, I seem to know at once how to create the sounds."

"And you will!" Ghiretti chuckled. "Imagination and genius are one and the same! *'Le style est l'homme même.'*"

"The style," Nicolò translated, "is the man himself."

"Bravo!" Ghiretti gazed at the ceiling. "The best way to develop it is not to think about it."

"Not to?" Nicolò threw up his hands. "Then how do you get it?"

Ghiretti hunched forward. "Are you familiar with the term 'turning the stilus'?"

"Never heard of it." Nicolò put his elbows on the table, resting his chin in his hands. "What does it mean?"

"The old Romans," Ghiretti explained, "engraved on tablets of wax with a tool of metal, wood, or ivory called a stilus, which was sharp on one end, blunt on the other. Whenever the scribes changed what they'd written with the point by 'erasing' with the stub, they were 'turning the stilus.' Now —" Ghiretti's violet eyes sparkled — "when a violinist turns the stilus, he corrects and criticizes his playing, improving his interpretation. As the Roman's personality was revealed by his drawings in the wax, you are expressed by your stilus, the bow, when you draw it across the strings." Ghiretti added, "Didn't Voltaire say, 'The ear is the road to the heart'? Play from your heart, lad! And your interpretation will speak to all hearts!"

On a wintry afternoon, in Germi's lodgings near the University, Nicolò said, "I am getting along so rapidly, I can't say how it's all happening!" He added, honestly, "We've seen each other hardly at all, but it doesn't matter. I know you're close by."

"We're growing up, *amico*. Our paths are dividing. Careers, circumstances, many things may separate us, but we shall always be friends."

Back at Ghiretti's, he wasn't surprised to find the house empty. More than likely the maestro was sitting again for Pasini, the portrait painter. "Glad to have something to do," he'd told Nicolò. "There's time to kill, these days. The court's not as gay as it used to be with Ferdinando and Marie Amalia off on their country estates." The front door slammed.

"You're back early," Nicolò greeted him.

"To fetch you." Ghiretti's face was determined. "Bring your instrument."

"Why?" Nicolò put on his coat.

"I'll show him! He can say good-bye to it now!"

None of it made sense, but Nicolò knew it was useless to prod. Ghiretti, like his grandfather, would get to it in his own time. When they were on the street, Ghiretti said, "I told him you'd accept any challenge."

Nicolò asked, "Who do you mean?"

"Why, Pasini, of course! All the while he paints, I speak of you. I tell him that at Rolla's I heard the voice of heaven!"

"Hm," Nicolò said, hoping it qualified for whatever the maestro wanted to hear.

"Let me finish!" Ghiretti's eyes flashed. "He says to me, 'Your enthusiasm is colored by pride in your own teaching.' He dabs at his palette, smugly mixing paints. 'No boy can be that great. I am a fair musician, myself. I know!' And then he laughs." Ghiretti's jaw sharpened. "Do you hear, boy? He laughs at Ghiretti!"

"But —" Nicolò was silenced by a look.

"'Musician,' I say. 'Ha! Beside him you're only a miserable scraper of sheep's guts!'" Ghiretti smiled. "Then guess what he says?"

"I couldn't possibly guess."

"'Why do you hide this Paganini? Where is he? Bring him here. If he accepts a challenge I have in mind, it may be worth his while.'" They went under an archway. "Ah!" Ghiretti said, "we're here."

Pasini stopped cleaning his brushes when he saw them. "So you're Paganini?" Smiling, he came forward, ignoring Ghiretti but including him just the same. "I'm sure the stories about you are exaggerated." He glanced drolly at the maestro, whose expression was inscrutable. "That's what I have to find out!" He was a man of average height, thin but not frail, with eyes that sparkled deviltry as though

140

something teased him inside. His hair, dark and coarse, was even darker and coarser on the backs of his hands. "Is it true," he asked, "that you played Rolla's concerto from sight?"

"A part of it — the solo, yes, sir."

"Ghiretti, here, says that you can play anything, even if you've never seen it. Is that so?" Nicolò considered the question.

"I've no reason to think otherwise," he replied.

"Very well." Pasini summoned a manservant and spoke to him softly. After the servant left the room he said, "I challenge you, Paganini, to play, right now, a certain work of Viotti's."

"I have studied Viotti, sir. It is possible that this composition will not be unknown to me."

"Thank you," Pasini applauded, "but you've never seen this score. It is unpublished. Moreover, it's supposed to be his most difficult. I came upon it by accident." The servant brought in a cherry-wood stand, handing the score to Pasini. Nicolò wrinkled his forehead.

"I accept your challenge," he said. "I don't intend to lose. What are your terms?"

"If you're unable to play this —" Pasini flipped the score — "then you will give a series of concerts, here, as many as I choose, for my friends." Pasini arched his brows. "You haven't asked what happens if you win."

"I had hoped you would tell me."

"Ho, ho! Well said!" Pasini laughed. "So I am a miserable scraper of sheep's guts, am I? Therefore . . . in my possession a fine fiddle goes to waste. In the future I will confine myself to my brushes." He shrugged. "I am saying that my Stradivari is yours if —"

"A Stradivari?" Nicolò's blood pounded in his ears. "A Cremona — Stradivari — violin?" His voice squeaked and his legs dissolved. He sat down.

"Get hold of yourself!" Ghiretti cried. "Don't fall apart now. You'll not make me a liar."

Nicolò fingered the snuffbox in his pocket. Then he stepped to the stand, tightened the hair of his bow with a twist of the knob. He placed the violin under his chin, closed his eyes for a moment to pray, then said: "I am ready."

Pasini placed the score before him. Glancing knowingly over the page, Nicolò breathed more freely. The music was difficult, but not nearly as complicated as scores he had written himself.

Even before he was off to a good start, Pasini's mouth flew open. Forgetting to seat himself, he stood motionless, his eyes fixed on Nicolò's flying fingers. Ghiretti smiled victoriously. The servant came in again, gaping. A man outside crossed the street, came nearer to listen. At the close, Pasini applauded.

"Bravo! *Viva il maestro!*" Suddenly he grinned sheepishly. "Why am I so happy? I've just lost a fine violin!" He hurried out of the room, returning almost immediately and bowing deeply, placed the Stradivari in Nicolò's hands. "You were born to enchant the world, Paganini!" he said. "I am honored that Pasini's violin can be a part of that enchantment."

Nicolò couldn't speak. He took the instrument gingerly,

turned it over and over, awestruck by its symmetry, its perfectly proportioned body, graceful as a fine lady. Two matched pieces of maple formed the back, their curly grain identical. The front, exquisite in flowing side *c*'s and slanting *f*'s. He stroked the surface, admiring its lustrous varnish, ebony fingerboard, the long thin throat, the carved scroll. Pasini's face swam before him.

"My lips won't behave," Nicolò said, hoarsely. He cradled the violin, warming it with his hands. Pasini nodded. Ghiretti blew his nose. Unable to refrain a moment longer, Nicolò tucked the violin under his chin, picked up the bow. He played a long singing note on the G string. The sound floated harmoniously, rich and sweet. He said gravely, "I accept it with humility. . . . It is mine, only to dedicate its message to all people, everywhere!"

144

12

When Germi was informed of the event at Pasini's, he said, with characteristic loyalty, "We must celebrate! High time we started spreading your fame. How can you conquer the world if you're known only to Genoa?" He grinned. As one they made for the desk, cried out in unison:

"Paper! To make plans!" Free from lectures the following week, Germi printed posters announcing the Parma concert. Ghiretti made buckets of paste. The three of them posted the notices all over town.

The afternoon before the performance, as they returned from rehearsal with the accompanist, Germi ran ahead, zigzagging out of Nicolò's reach. Nicolò jumped a pile of debris and landed, *wham!* on a pain that shot all the way to his jaw.

"My foot! Germi!" he yelled. "I've punctured my foot!"

"Keep your weight off it!" Germi was at his side. "Hang onto me!" With his arm around Germi's shoulders, Nicolò made it by hopping on his good foot. At home, his heel, throbbing in earnest, began to swell. It even hurt when Ghiretti pulled off his stocking.

"Water!" the maestro cried. "And barley to make a poultice!" They soaked his foot and examined it. A nail. . . . Ghiretti frowned, "Rotten luck, Nicolò. I doubt if you can perform —"

Nicolò sat up in bed. "I'll play," he said, "if I have to be carried on the stage."

That wasn't necessary, though it probably would have been wiser. When Nicolò hobbled onto the stage he was greeted by catcalls and howls of laughter. Gritting his teeth partly from pain, partly from anger, he realized that since his normal appearance struck most strangers as peculiar — tonight, with his clumsy limp, he must look ludicrous to them. Nevertheless, he had no intention of sounding a note until they were quiet. And his mind worked fast, searching for a dramatic method of silencing them. As the idea occurred, he winked at his accompanist, who was obviously flustered by the rude reception. The poor man mopped his face and tried to smile.

Nicolò touched the candles on either side of his music stand, snuffing out the flames with his fingers. A hush spread instantly but now there were snickers and whispers. All right, if they were going to whisper, he'd give them something to whisper about. Lifting the music stand, he limped with it to the back of the ramp where he left it. Now there wasn't a sound. They were probably wondering whether he could play without his music. Well, they would soon find out. Besides, there was nothing to fear. The snuffbox was safe in his pocket, and wasn't his the *only* instrument a virtuoso should play?

He drew a singing note on the G string, opening with a light melody — and the audience was his. He was well into his second number when the upper string broke. The crowd went into new gales of merriment. Nicolò's mouth dried up. A pulse beat in his temple. Without missing a note, he played right along on three strings. People sat forward, craning to see. A few began to applaud. He sprayed *staccati* with a springing bow. And the second string broke! The audience was in hysterics. He was a joke! He, Nicolò Paganini, was a laughingstock! With fury, he went ahead on the two remaining strings. The audience sucked in its breath. Nicolò smiled to himself. Might as well give them their money's worth. In a moment, now, he'd show them something they'd never forget.

At the end of the composition — deliberately — he broke the third string! There was one united gasp. Nicolò nodded to his accompanist, who was glued to his seat. Nicolò nodded twice before he raised his fingers to the keys.

On the G string alone, he played his final number to a standing audience. Wringing wet, he limped off the stage to the cries of "Bravo!" — whistles and shouts — and not once did he cover his ears to shut out the sound.

At the small party, later, at Pasini's, exclamations of disbelief continued. "Wouldn't surprise me," someone said, "if he could play without any strings at all!"

"Let's see!" Germi crossed to a bespectacled gentleman. *"Perdone, signor,* may I?" The astonished man handed over his eyeglasses. Removing the silk cord, Germi winked at Nicolò. "And, now, Maestro," he said, "your bow, if you please." In high glee, Nicolò limped to the punchbowl. And when his friend had stretched the cord across its rim, with expert dexterity, he applied the bow. A weird, sighing note arose as laughter drowned out the sound. They didn't see the servant enter. He stood there, nervously wait-ing to be noticed. Pasini looked up.

"Yes, Luigi, what is it?"

"Outside, I just heard a courier." Luigi licked his lips. "Napoleon is marching into Piedmont. The French army is on Italian soil!"

Nobody spoke. Nicolò looked from one face to another. There was surprise, relief, fear. Finally someone stammered, "Piedmont? They came from the Apennines? Through the ice and snow? It's not possible!"

"Although there are those who welcome the invading army and believe in its mission," Ghiretti said, "this news has but one meaning, *war!*"

At home, Nicolò thought, First, Napoleon's a French general acclaimed for defeating England; then, he's a prisoner of France, arrested for treason and now he leads her army into Italy to fight Austria and Sardinia! What does it all mean? It makes me dizzy just to think of it.

During the following weeks, conversation in Parma dealt with two topics only. Ghiretti told Nicolò, "One minute the talk is only of Paganini — his nerve-splitting harmonics, his one-string concert. In the next breath, it's Napoleon, his indomitable leadership with a handful of half-starved soldiers. Both of you are reserving a page in history!" Pasini added, "He's changed the spelling of his name to Bonaparte. Now he's French!"

"Then he's no longer proud to be Italian!"

Nicolò didn't know he'd been heard until Pasini replied, "I think not. In the wake of his military operations, Italians are finding it impossible to obtain proper food and clothing — suffering, too, under heavy contributions levied."

Much later, in bed, Nicolò said half aloud: "It's plain to me, General. This is what you were planning that evening, in Genoa. You've taken your first step in conquering the world, just as I will be taking mine soon — a concert tour. But why did you change your name? We're less alike than I thought, General. . . ."

On May 15th, Parma was rocked by further news. Napoleon had entered Milan to the cheers of a jubilant population. Germi said, "When the Archbishop, with princes and dukes, met him and his dilapidated army at the gates, Bonaparte said, 'France wishes the Lombards well.' But he is a liar!"

"Why?" Nicolò dipped his quill in the ink, completing the score.

"Why?" Germi threw up his hands. "Don't you know what's going on? How can you be so calm in the middle of a world that's upside down? Oh, don't answer! You're not conscious of anything, but —"

"He may prefer to be French." Nicolò laid the quill on the table. "But that doesn't make him a liar."

"Well, listen to this. When the King of Sardinia agreed to

an armistice, Napoleon asked to be received with trust, said, 'The French nation is a friend of all nations.' He said they would wage war like generous enemies, that their only quarrel was 'with the tyrants who enslaved you!' "

Nicolò interrupted. "What's wrong with that? He freed the Piedmontese —"

"Freed? He transferred them from one tyrant to another! The same in Lombardy. A few days in Milan was all he needed to set up a republican government. Now he is saying, 'I will protect you but I am your master!' At a reception he informed them, 'I will choose fifty men to rule Lombardy in the name of France. Such is my will.' " Germi was talking so fast, little sprays of saliva shot from his lips. He stopped to swallow, then continued: "Such is my will. Ha! The Lombards aren't free, they're — they're French! Napoleon is a symbol of evil, a dictator, a despot!" Germi shook his finger. "When he said the army of France has come to break your Austrian chains, he forgot to add, so that French chains can be attached! He sold Italy out! There's no telling what that demon traitor will do next!"

"We've always been under somebody's thumb," Nicolò reminded his friend. "Italy has always had war and an enemy. What else has the General done, besides bring more of the same?"

"Isn't that enough? But it isn't all! He's sending home wagonloads of trophies and loot! He's looting art treasures for the Louvre. These goings-on are supervised by a 'governmental commission for the research of artistic and scientific objects in conquered countries.' Can you imagine?"

Germi's voice shook. "Does that high-sounding title give him a license to steal? And gold! Gold that he's extracted from princes by terms of the truce!"

Nicolò said, "But —"

"How do you think Duke Ferdinando bought neutrality? With two million francs — cash! Bonaparte acts as though he owned the world. And horses!" Germi screamed. "Napoleon's sending *Italian* horses to Paris!"

The front door slammed as Ghiretti burst in from Pasini's. "The portrait's terrible," he said. "Looks exactly like me!" He removed his cloak. "The afternoon was cut short by the excitement. Wait!" he held up a hand. "Let me tell you!" He turned to Nicolò. "Do you know a Colonel Livron?"

Nicolò sprang up. "From Leghorn?"

"He's Commissioner of Supply for Napoleon!" Ghiretti said. That explained his meeting with Bonaparte, Nicolò thought. "His carriage broke down in front of Pasini's house. He was in a terrible hurry to get along. We persuaded him to come inside while it was being repaired." Ghiretti laughed. "I don't recall how your name came up, but when he learned that you were in Parma he dashed into the garden, returning a few seconds later. Then he did a funny thing."

"What?"

"Now what did I do with it?" Ghiretti felt in his pocket. "He said to give this to you. That you'd understand." The maestro leaned over and placed a blue flower in Nicolò's hand. . . .

Late that evening, when Germi opened the door of his room, he said, "Nicolò! What're you doing here? At this time of night — with your violin? Well, come in! Don't just stand there!"

"Germi, there's something wrong in Leghorn."

"How on earth did you conjure that up?"

"The flower —"

"Doesn't prove a thing!" Germi scratched his chin. "Lisa said she'd send you a reminder to visit them. The Colonel was in a hurry this afternoon. Probably couldn't take the time to invite you personally, so he chose this method. It's just what he would do — because it was her idea. Here, sit down."

"I don't think so. I wish I could, but I can't." Nicolò remained standing. "Germi, I'm going to Leghorn."

"You're what? Your head is cracked!" Germi's eyes crinkled. "How, *amico?*" He felt in his pocket. "You're welcome to what money —"

"No thanks, Germi. You can help, though. I have decided to pawn my violin."

"Pawn your Stradivari? Does going mean that much to you? Why not the little violin?"

"I sent it home. A friend of Ghiretti's took it soon after I won this." Germi reached for his jacket.

"We'll have to wake a moneylender. Are you going to start out in the middle of the night?"

"I'll walk, catch a ride on a cart by morning, if I'm lucky — the stage. It doesn't matter. I'm going, that's all. I've already said good-bye to Ghiretti."

"Then we're wasting time. Come along!" As they went

out, Germi added, "I'll keep the pawn ticket. There'll be money soon from my father. I can redeem the violin and bring it to Genoa when the school term is over. Or leave it with Ghiretti. Whatever you say."

"Bring it home. I won't return to Parma. It's time to spread out."

"Good idea!" Germi laughed. "I'll see you in Genoa. We'll schedule your first road tour!"

Nicolò left Parma on foot, under a full moon that silver-coated the night. He carried the bundle of personal possessions which he'd removed from the violin case. His hand felt strangely empty without the Stradivari. Thinking of this and listening to rustlings and private noises of small animals, he kept his mind off the fear that invaded him whenever he thought of Lisa. True to his prediction, at dawn, a cart creaked alongside. The peddler rubbed his eyes.

"A lad — out here alone? How did you get away from your mother?"

"I am not a lad. I am Nicolò Paganini."

"Well, you don't say! Glad to meet you! I am Napoleon Bonaparte!"

"But I *am* Paganini. May I ride with you? I am tired."

"Paganini?" The driver looked at his hands. "Without a violin? That's a joke. If you had it, I could make room. I like to be entertained." Nicolò touched the bundle.

"I have money. And I can hum!"

"Well, now — money?" The driver gave him a hand. "Hop in. I myself am a singer!" He opened his mouth and the hills rocked with a deep bass. Nicolò picked up the tune.

153

The driver slapped the reins against the donkey's back and the cart groaned on. At the next posting station, Nicolò bade the peddler good-bye and boarded the stage. . . .

Colonel Livron's castle stood in the center of a vast estate. Stables ranged off the right, a winding road circled a rose garden. Barely noticing the details, Nicolò hurried past the carriages. He felt a little foolish. Now that he was here, what would he say?

There was no opportunity to say anything. "Paganini! Welcome!" Livron threw open the door, practically carried him inside. "Good lad!" He smiled broadly. "I see you got my message." Taking a vigorous turn across the foyer, he peered down a hall, came back to say, conspiratorially, "I didn't tell Lisa and the others for fear you'd not arrive."

"The others?" Nicolò said. And then he heard it; lively conversation, laughter. The house was full of people!

"Well, come along!" Livron swept him through the hall into a room that belonged in a palace.

"Nicolò!" Lisa flew across the floor. "How absolutely marvelous! How did you know?" The Colonel winked over her head. "Now my birthday is perfect!" Her dress was the color of fresh raspberries. She took his arm. "You must meet everybody. I've told them so much about you. . . ."

The next half hour Nicolò's hand was pumped, his back slapped, his shoulder pounded. Even Cat came in, rubbed against his legs as if to say, It's about time! Finally, Lisa took him aside.

"The Silver Étude, Nicolò," she said. "They know all about this étude. They're so anxious to hear it. Will you play for us?" Nicolò almost collapsed. Play? He couldn't play for her, and he'd never tell her why. It was too embarrassing. The room was suddenly very warm. He looked desperately around for air. Livron was staring at him from a big armchair. Lisa waited expectantly, a smile on her face.

Nicolò could only mumble something unintelligible. What could he say? Livron rose and sauntered over to them as though he were out for a stroll.

"Give him up, for a moment, Lisa." The Colonel spoke casually. "I'll return him soon."

"Very well, Father! But don't keep him too long." Then she moved on to other guests.

"It isn't difficult to guess why you're uncomfortable," Livron said. Uncomfortable? Nicolò squirmed. He was positively miserable. "When you came in, I noticed you were without your instrument. Why, doesn't concern me. Because I cannot play, I content myself with collecting violins, anticipating the pleasure of my guests. So. . . ." The Colonel inclined his head. "Follow me!" It seemed as if they had walked several miles before he opened a heavy door. One wall of the area, large and square, held an array of swords, a brace of pistols, a few muskets. On the opposite side, a built-in compartment ran end to end. It was crowded with instruments. Nicolò could scarcely breathe. Never had he seen such a collection. "Among them are several Stradivari," Livron said. "And an Amati with a rotund belly. I'm told it's rare. Take your choice." Speechless, Nicolò looked from one to the other, trying to make up his mind. Livron lifted one from a peg. "Try this," he said. "It should be in perfect tune." He extended the bow.

Nicolò lowered his eyes as he placed the violin under his chin. Suddenly, he grew rigid.

"What's the matter?" Livron followed his glance. "You've seen a rat before, haven't you?"

"That violin — in the corner, by itself. . . ." Nicolò could barely control his excitement. It was larger than the others. The *f* holes weren't the same size.

"Oh, that!" Livron laughed. "Queer-looking, isn't it? Not uniform. And the sound holes. As if they were cut with a dull knife!"

Nicolò was trembling. "Please, may I see it?" Eagerly he took the instrument from Livron's hands. "Look!" he shouted. "The wide slot of the head — the glimmering varnish. And the *f* hole is larger on the bass side! This is *it!*" he cried. "The one he made for the jailer's daughter!"

"I haven't the faintest notion as to why you are so excited," Livron said. "I bought this violin from a friend who'd bought it from a friend. It was highly recommended, I can't think why. It's tone is — sour! My friend said it was a Guarneri. Who knows?"

"I do! And I know how to prove it. Take it to the window! Hold it so that the light shines into the *f* hole on the bass-bar side." The Colonel's eyebrows rose. "The one on this side," Nicolò explained, and licked his lips. "Now," he said, when the Colonel had reached the window and was squinting, with the violin at an angle close to his face, "you should see a label on a wooden block!"

"So it is! And a cross scratched in ink!"

"And," Nicolò said, "the holy initials, I.H.S. The year, 1743."

156

"Yes! How did you know?"

"Sir," Nicolò exulted, "you are holding in your hands a Joseph del Gesu Guarneri! About the rarest violin in the whole world!"

Livron marveled. "And all the while I've had it here gathering dust! Well, it deserves a master." He pointed to a box. "Fresh strings," he explained. "I buy them in Genoa."

"Probably the ones I smelled boiling last summer." Nicolò laughed happily as he replaced the old strings. Then he tested the Guarneri. The magnificent tone echoed to the far walls. It did seem a little sour. He adjusted the tuning and brought the bow across the strings. Ah! This violin would be majestic in a large hall, a massive theater! This violin could handle the strange new kind of music he wrote. What he would give to own this instrument! He played the scales in thirds, then in sixths. Only a few minutes to get the feel. . . . Upstairs, they were waiting. He smiled, "I am ready, sir."

A few days later, when he'd said a proper good-bye to Lisa, Nicolò ran down the steps to the waiting carriage. It had plum-red wheels and silver door handles. Wearing a smile all over his face, Livron extended a violin case. "For you, Paganini. The Guarneri. Please do me the courtesy to accept it."

Courtesy? Accept? Nicolò held the case as if it would break. His heart ran over, his throat closed. "Colonel, sir —" He could only stammer. "There are not enough words in any language to say —"

Livron laughed. "You've already said it! You'll say it every time you touch your violin. Good-bye, Paganini!"

Nicolò climbed inside as the driver jumped onto the box. With a crack of the whip, the carriage swung past the garden, along the road, turned toward Genoa. Nicolò held the precious Guarneri on his knees. Then he put his arms around it, hugging it to him. Closing his eyes, he stretched his legs, settling into a corner. The steady *clop-clop* of the horses' hoofs beat a happy tune. Smiling contentedly, he thought back over the years. . . . Adventures, new friends, new understanding of people, and of himself.

Lisa . . . who'd first awakened him to the real meaning and source of beauty, who showed him that the most discerning eye was the heart. Beethoven . . . who taught that life is joy and sadness together. Di Negro . . . unselfishly applying his "polish" — his penetration of humanity, its aspirations, its fears. Nicolò leaned his head back farther into the seat. His father — big and boisterous and determined, who kept his real feelings hidden away. All of his teachers . . . their foibles, discipline, and patience. Marchesi . . . wonderful, unique Marchesi! And his mother . . . who asked only to love him. Germi . . . who was the complete definition of rich, warm friendship, that neither distance or separation changed. Finally, Napoleon . . . winning nothing that really mattered — only hate and fear. The General would find out one day that the tragedy of life was what happens to a man's insides when a part of him dies so he cannot feel the joy and pain of other men! Napoleon. . . .

Nicolò moved his foot. Pins and needles ran along the

sole. He yawned. Evidently he'd been asleep, for outside, the sea sparkled blue and beautiful, and salt air tickled his nose. Home — he was nearly home! The Duomo stood like a welcoming sentinel. And there, coming into view, was the lofty Porto Soprano with its rounded towers. He could almost hear the bustle from the market square, the laughter of the *legabelle.* . . .

Nicolò sat up straighter. Hearts couldn't be captured, like countries, with a flag dictating allegiance! Hearts were to be unlocked — with a golden key! And that key was love and music — music played on a Guarneri — his Guarneri. Love was belonging to people and having them belong to you! And now, he knew. He belonged to the world! To all people, everywhere. His music would bring laughter and tears, call forth shadows and light, pain and joy. He would be forgotten and remembered, ridiculed and praised. But now, today, and the day after and the day after that — he had so much to do!

Nicolò leaned far out the window. Tangy air filled his lungs. He cupped his hand over his mouth and yelled to the driver in front:

"Can you go a little faster, please? A Paganini is on his way to fulfill a vision!"